The Aircraft Performance Requirements Manual

R. V. Davies

Airlife
England

Copyright © 1991 by R. V. Davies

First published in the UK in 1991
by Airlife Publishing Ltd

British Library Cataloguing in Publication Data
Davies, R. V.
   The aircraft performance requirements manual.
   1. Aircraft. Flying
   I. Title
   629.13252

   ISBN 1 85310 168 0

Printed by Livesey Ltd., Shrewsbury

Airlife Publishing Ltd.

101 Longden Road, Shrewsbury SY3 9EB

Contents

Bibliography

Aeronautical Information Publication — U.K. (AIP) — The U.K.
    Air Pilot
Aeronautical Information Circular(s) — U.K. (AIC)
Air Navigation (General) Regulations— AN(G)R
Air Navigation Order 1989   — ANO
British Civil Airworthiness Requirements — BCAR — Section K
CAP   32 — Meteorology Section of the U.K. AIP
CAP 168 — Licensing of Aerodromes
CAP 360 — Air Operator's Certificate — Requirements. Vols 1
    and 2
CAP 513 — Extended Range Twin Operations (ETOPS)
General Aviation Safety Leaflet No. 7 — Aeroplane Performance
ICAO Type A Chart(s)
Joint Airworthiness Requirements — JAR— 1
                                       — 25

Specimen Performance Charts:
Group A   CAP 385
       C   CAP 551
       D
       E   CAP 508
Summary of Aeroplane Performance Requirements — 1981

Foreword

The purpose of this guide is to provide information relating to the Air Navigation (General) Regulations, Joint Airworthiness Requirements and the British Civil Airworthiness Requirements in conjunction with the aeroplane Flight Manual, so that students of aeroplane performance and operating pilots may better understand the criteria involved in the determination of aeroplane operating weights.

The Air Navigation (General) Regulations — AN(G)R — consist, in part, of a set of flight safety rules whereby the limiting operating weight of the aeroplane is determined in accordance with detailed parameters and conditions appropriate to the phase of flight. Joint Airworthiness Requirements (JAR) and British Civil Airworthiness Requirements (BCAR) consist of sections devoted to the complete range of aeroplane design and construction, and also detail the minimum performance requirements, under specific conditions, to be satisfied before aeroplane certification.

The level of safety intended by the airworthiness performance requirements will be achieved only by relating the flight characteristics of the aeroplane to the characteristics of the aerodrome, the terrain close to the aerodrome, the route to be flown and the ambient conditions prevailing at the time. The level of safety will be achieved when the aeroplane, certified in accordance with the requirements, is operated in accordance with the information contained in the aeroplane Flight Manual, in conjunction with the appropriate operating rules of the AN(G)R.

It is stressed that, although much of the information contained herein has been derived from CAA publications, the interpretation of rules, regulations etc., are strictly the author's. Opinions, recommendations and/or conclusions contained herein should *not* be construed as official CAA policy or practice.

Unclassified and Performance Group X aeroplanes are not mentioned in this guide, since new aeroplanes will no longer be certified in these groups.

R. V. Davies 1991.

SECTION ONE

1. Introduction

1.1 The weight and performance requirements in respect of aeroplanes engaged in public transport are contained in the Air Navigation (General) Regulations (AN(G)R) and are made under the powers derived from the Air Navigation Order (ANO). A number of articles of the ANO combine to form the powers referred to in the following manner:

(i) Article 7 states that an aircraft shall not fly unless there is in force a valid Certificate of Airworthiness (C of A) in respect thereof.

(ii) Article 8(2) states that the C of A shall specify such categories appropriate to the aircraft in accordance with Schedule 3, for example Transport — Passenger or Cargo, Aerial Work, etc. The schedule also designates the purpose for which the aircraft may fly.

(iii) Article 8(4) states that the C of A may designate the performance group to which the aircraft belongs for the purpose of Article 29(1).

(iv) Article 29(1) outlines the requirements in respect of the aircraft weight and related performance, specific meteorological conditions and night flights.

(v) Article 29(2) specifies that the assessment of the ability of an aircraft to comply with 29(1) shall be based on the information contained in the C of A.

Thus the weight and performance requirements consist of two distinct but complementary aspects: Airworthiness Requirements — Articles 7 and 8; and Operational Requirements — Article 29.

However, before considering both, an overall picture of the Performance Requirements should be considered.

1.2 The requirements, as promulgated in the AN(G)R, basically constitute a set of flight safety rules, designed to ensure that an aeroplane, undertaking a public transport flight is despatched at a safe weight. The requirements are concerned only with the despatch weight in the belief that if this is correctly determined, the conduct of the flight can be left to the pilot, who will be unlikely to have to make critical performance decisions in situations where he is under pressure.

1.3 The word 'unlikely' is important since performance requirements are concerned with probabilities, based on the scale shown in Table 1.1. The listed probabilities are on an hourly, or per flight basis, whichever is the more appropriate.

Table 1.1

Description	Probability	Example
Frequent. Likely to occur often during the life of each aeroplane.	10^{-3}	
Reasonably Probable. Unlikely to occur often but may occur several times during the life of each aeroplane.		Engine failure.
	10^{-5}	
Remote. Unlikely to occur to each aeroplane during its life but may occur several times during the life of a number of aeroplanes of the same type.		Low speed over-run. Failing to achieve net take-off flight path. Minor damage. Possible passenger injuries.
	10^{-7}	
Extremely Remote. Possible but unlikely to occur in the total life of a number of aeroplanes of the same type.		High speed over-run. Ditching. Extensive damage. Possible loss of life. Double engine failure on a twin-engined aeroplane. Hitting obstacle in the net take-off flight path.
	10^{-9}	
Should not happen, or 'extremely improbable'.		Aeroplane destroyed — multiple deaths

2. Airworthiness Requirements

2.1 All public transport aeroplanes on the UK register are certified according to the appropriate airworthiness code: Joint Airworthiness Requirements (JAR), or British Civil Airworthiness Requirements (BCAR), in the performance groups as listed in Table 2.1. JAR and BCAR consist of sections devoted to the complete range of aircraft design and construction and, in relation to this guide, the important sections are: JAR — 25; or BCAR Section D (Large Aeroplanes), Section K (Light Aeroplanes). Some authorities may consider the requirements of JAR 25 applicable also to aeroplanes of less than 5700 kg, having ten or more passenger seats. JAR 25 does not contain requirements for reciprocating engines or seaplanes, or

Table 2.1

Performance Group	Code	Aeroplane Types	Performance Data	Example
A	JAR 25	Large multi-engined	Flight Manual	Boeing 727, 737, 747, 757, A 300 series
C	BCAR K	Multi-engined to 5700 kg	Flight Manual	Cessna, Piper and Beech twin-engined
D	BCAR K	Single-engined and some low performance twin-engined	Flight Manual	Auster, some Cessna and Piper single-engined
E	BCAR K	Single-engined and twins up to 2730 kg	Flight Manual, Owner's Manual, or Pilot's Operating Handbook	Cessna single-engined

credit for standby power, for example rockets. Before a C of A is granted, the certification within the appropriate code must be satisfied.

1

An integral part of the C of A is the aeroplane Flight Manual which is vetted and approved by the CAA's Airworthiness Division of the Safety Regulation Group, and contains limits within which the aeroplane *must* be operated, and the performance data required to show compliance with the despatch rules of the AN(G)R.

All airworthiness requirements in respect of Performance Group A aeroplanes contained in this document are based on JAR 25.

2.2 The main differences between the performance groups are as follows:

Group A
The most stringent of airworthiness requirements, with a performance level accounting for engine failure during *all* stages of flight.

Group C
Accountability for engine failure, except during take-off and initial climb, and on the final stages of the approach, i.e. from approximately 200 ft at the departure aerodrome to approximately 200 ft at the destination aerodrome.

Group D
No specific provision for engine failure.

Group E
A performance level similar to Group C (twin-engined), or Group D (single-engined).

NEW PERFORMANCE GROUPS
In the near future the Authority intends to introduce new Performance Regulations applicable to new Performance Group Classifications of aeroplanes, which are:

Group B
Aeroplanes, having a MTWA not exceeding 5700 kg and not having more than 19 passenger seats; the performance level will be such that a forced landing is unlikely to be necessary in the event of engine failure at any point in the flight. The Regulations applicable to this group are envisaged to be the same as those applying to Group A aeroplanes, i.e. AN(G)R 7, with some minor differences.

Group F

It is anticipated that this Group will include both single and twin engined aeroplanes, under the following specifications:

(a)   Single engine aeroplanes having a MTWA not exceeding 5700 kg and not having more than 9 passenger seats.

(b)   twin engined aeroplanes having a MTWA not exceeding 5700 kg and not having more than 9 passenger seats; the performance level will be such that a forced landing may be necessary following engine failure shortly after lift-off or shortly before landing.

Regulations applicable to this Group will be new, but some similarities with existing AN(G)R 8 — Group C, and AN(G)R 10 — Group E — may be noted.

Note

The aeroplane examples given under Performance Group A have been certified under the requirements of BCAR, Section D.

3. Operational Requirements

3.1   As stated, Article 29 outlines the requirements to be prescribed in respect of the weight and performance of an aeroplane engaged in public transport. The AN(G)R complements these requirements by presenting a set of despatch rules, aimed at providing a maximum take-off weight (RTOW) which, in the known or reported meteorological conditions at take-off, and the expected en-route and landing meteorological conditions, will result in an acceptable and broadly uniform level of safety.

3.2   The RTOW is the lowest weight derived from consideration of the following:

(a)   Maximum authorised take-off weight (structural limit)

(b)   Maximum take-off weight for aerodrome altitude and temperature (WAT — take-off climb limit)

(c)   Take-off field lengths

(d) Obstacle clearance

(e) En-route capability

(f) Landing weight for aerodrome altitude and temperature (WAT — landing climb limit)

(g) Landing field lengths

(h) Maximum authorised landing weight (structural limit)

(i) Tyre speed limit

(j) Brake energy limit

(k) Other airworthiness limitations, for example maximum quick turn-round weight.

Of the items listed above, it may be noted that *a* and *h* to *k* inclusive are airworthiness limits; whilst *b* to *g* inclusive are covered by the provisions of the AN(G)R. The list also serves to illustrate the complementary aspects of the two sets of requirements.

3.3 Table 3.1 outlines the regulations applicable to each performance group for the respective phase of flight,

Table 3.1
Take-off weight — Summary of Regulations
(All references are to the AN(G)R, except where stated)

	Performance Groups			
	A	**C**	**D**	**E**
Take-off				
(a) WAT graph/curve climb limit	7(1)	8(1)	9(1)	(10)(1) (a)
(b) Field lengths	7(2)	8(2)	9(2)	(10)(1) (b)
(c) Flight path				
(i) all engines operative	—	8(3)	9(3)	—
(ii) one engine inoperative	7(3)	8(4)	—	—
En-route				
(a) one engine inoperative	7(4)	8(5)	9(4)	(10)(1) (c)
(b) two engines inoperative	7(5)	—	—	—
Landing				
(a) WAT graph/curve (climb limit)	7(6)	8(6)	9(5)	(10)(1) (d)
(b) Field length	7(7)	8(7)	9(6)	(10)(1) (e)
Operational limitations				
(a) Weather conditions	—	8(4)	9	(10)(2)
(b) Night flight	—	—	9	(10)(2)
General				
ANO Art. 29(3)				

including operational requirements. It can be noted that operational limitations increase in severity as performance capability decreases. For example, for a Group C aeroplane, during the initial climb (the take-off flight path), for obstacle clearance purposes the aeroplane is deemed to have one engine inoperative on entering cloud, or when restricted visibility precludes obstacle clearance by visual means; a Group D aeroplane may not fly for public transport purposes at night or when the cloud base is below 1000 ft, or the visibility is less than one nautical mile at departure, destination or alternate aerodromes. The same applies to Group E aeroplanes with a relatively poor rate of climb.

3.4   There may be additional constraints on the planned flight which are not strictly performance aspects, for example noise abatement procedures. Personnel involved in the despatch of aeroplanes should familiarise themselves with these constraints, including information contained in NOTAMS, AIC, Airworthiness Notices and CAP 360 — the Air Operators Certificate publication — which contains guidance on flight planning, selection of alternate aerodromes and weather minima.

3.5   Compliance with airworthiness limitations is **mandatory** under the ANO, irrespective of the AN(G)R applicable to the flight. Use of the performance data associated with certification is **mandatory** when required by the AN(G)R; its use is generally desirable on all flights in the interest of safety in order to comply with Article 32 of the ANO, which covers the necessary pre-flight actions to be taken by the aircraft commander.

4. The Aerodrome

4.1   In order to determine the RTOW in accordance with the despatch rules it is necessary to have information in respect of the aerodromes of departure, destination and alternate(s) for take-off and landing. This information may be found in the Aeronautical Information Publication (AIP) of the country, or countries concerned. The contents of the UK AIP (The Air Pilot) are typical of the aerodrome data to be found in the documents.

4.2   The UK AIP 'Schedule of Aerodromes' gives comprehensive data of the runways at the listed aerodromes, which includes the 'declared' distances available for the Take-off Run, Take-off Distance, Emergency Distance and Landing Distance. In addition to the declared distances, the publication also gives the aerodrome elevation, and elevations of the start of each of the declared distances. From these given elevations, the slope values of the various distances may be calculated.

4.3   **Declared Distances**
The AN(G)R requires that where the distances are declared, they are the relevant distances for the purposes of the weight and performance requirements — 5. In the UK, for a distance to be declared it has to be notified in the Air Pilot or in a Notam, and also in accordance with the criteria contained in CAP 168 — Licensing of Aerodromes.

4.3.1   TAKE-OFF RUN AVAILABLE (TORA)
This and the other distances are defined in AN(G)R 5(3) thus:

> *the distance from the point on the surface of the aerodrome at which the aeroplane can commence its take-off run to the nearest point in the direction of take-off at which the surface of the aerodrome is incapable of bearing the weight of the aeroplane under normal operating conditions.*

Basically, this is the available runway length.

4.3.2   TAKE-OFF DISTANCE AVAILABLE (TODA)

> *the distance from the point on the surface of the aerodrome at which the aeroplane can commence its take-off run to the nearest obstacle in the direction of take-off projecting above the surface of the aerodrome and capable of affecting the safety of the aeroplane, or TORA × 1.5, whichever is the less.*

Basically, TODA consists of usable runway length plus **Clearway**.

4.3.2.1 Clearway
Clearway is defined in JAR 1 thus:

> *for turbine-engine powered aeroplanes, an area beyond the runway, not less than 152 metres wide (500 ft) centrally located about the extended centre-line of the runway and under control of the airport authorities. It is expressed in terms of a clearway plane extending from the end of the runway with an upward slope not exceeding 1.25%, above which no object or terrain protrudes. Threshold lights may protrude above this plane if their height above the end of the runway is 0.66 metres (26 inches) or less, and if located to each side of the runway.*

Thus clearway provides a symmetrically disposed area about the runway extended centreline in which an aeroplane can safely transit between lift-off and the required height at the end of take-off distance. Clearway need not have bearing strength, and may be land or water; also, within the clearway, minor surface irregularities are permitted, as are frangible objects less than 0.9 m (35.5 in) above local ground level. Clearway is not provided normally for runways less than 900 m long. A plan and elevation view of TORA and TODA is shown in Figure 4.1

4.3.3 EMERGENCY DISTANCE AVAILABLE (EDA)

> *the distance from the point on the surface of the aerodrome at which the aeroplane can commence its take-off run to the nearest point in the direction of take-off, at which the aeroplane cannot roll over the surface of the aerodrome and be brought to rest in an emergency without risk of accident.*

Basically, EDA consists of usable runway length, plus **Stopway**.

4.3.3.1 Stopway
Defined in JAR 1 thus:

> *an area beyond the take-off runway, no less wide than the runway and centred on the extended centreline of the runway, able to support the*

aeroplane during an aborted take-off without causing structural damage to the aeroplane and designated by the airport authorities for use in decelerating the aeroplane during an aborted take-off.

Since it is for occasional use only, it need not have the same wearing qualities of the runway it supplements; but note that it can exceed the length of the clearway. However, it should not have friction characteristics inferior to that of the runway. Figure 4.2 illustrates the plan and elevation views of the distances described, and their relationship.

4.3.4   LANDING DISTANCE AVAILABLE (LDA)

the distance from the point on the surface of the aerodrome upon which the aeroplane can commence its landing, having regard to the obstructions in its approach path, to the nearest point in the direction of landing at which the surface of the aerodrome is incapable of bearing the weight of the aeroplane under normal operating conditions, or at which there is an obstacle capable of affecting the safety of the aeroplane.

4.4   **Balanced Field Length (BFL)**
A balanced field exists if the TODA and EDA are equal. The balanced field length concept and its implications when used to determine take-off weight are more fully discussed in the specific Performance section.

4.5   **CAP 168 — Licensing of Aerodromes — Requirements**
The aerodrome licensing requirements of CAP 168 give greater detail of the criteria to be used for the determination of declared distances, the definitions of which correspond to those of the AN(G)R and JAR. However, CAP specifies in greater detail the criteria governing stopway and clearway (CAP 168 Chapter 3).

4.6   When determining the RTOW, the slopes of the declared distances must be taken into consideration (this should not be confused with the limiting slope as shown in Figures 4.1 and 4.2). The term 'slope' is used when referring to aerodrome surfaces or profiles, whereas gradient is used in reference to climb and descent profiles, although both are expressed in similar terms, i.e. percentage gradient or slope. In the absence of slope information, it may be calculated from the information referred to in 4.2, remembering that elevations are expressed in terms of feet above mean sea level, and horizontal distances are expressed in metres.

Slope may be calculated using the following formula:

$$\text{Slope (\%)} = \frac{\text{change in height (ft)}}{\text{horizontal distance} \times 3.28 \text{ (ft)}} \times 100$$

Figure 4.1

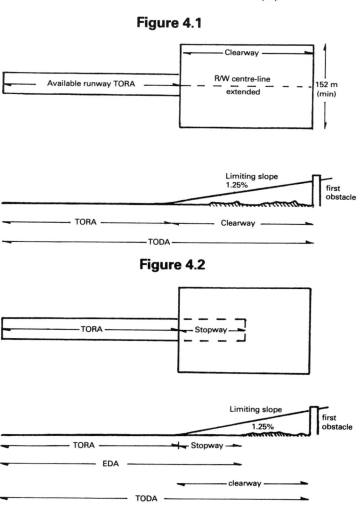

Figure 4.2

4.7   Obstruction Data

The Aerodrome Directory — aerodrome obstacles, in the AGA section of the UK AIP, gives a limited amount of data in respect of the obstructions in the vicinity of aerodromes. In general, this data provides information of the major obstructions within four nautical miles of the centre of the aerodrome, or aerodrome reference point and, exceptionally, beyond four nautical miles of the reference point. Other data includes information regarding high ground, power cables, etc. The information given, whilst of some use in the case of take-off, may be insufficient in respect of satisfying take-off flight path requirements. Thus, obstacles outside the scope of the AIP which have to be considered in the take-off flight path should be determined by reference to large scale maps, or, if available, ICAO Type A Charts.

4.7.1   ICAO Type A Charts

These charts provide the data necessary to enable operators to comply with the operating limitations of ICAO Annex 6 — Operation of Aircraft. The UK format of the chart complies with that given in ICAO Annex 4, and the ICAO Aeronautical Chart Manual, but the UK chart incorporates the additional safeguard whereby significant obstacles or obstructions are identified when a one per cent slope is penetrated.

Obstacle data illustrated on the charts extend to a surveyed distance of 15,000 m (8.1 nm) from the end of the runway or clearway, but the chart may terminate before this if no obstacles are present. In this context, where a Type A Chart carries a note to the effect that 'no obstructions exist beyond this point', the information is only valid up to 15,000 m from the end of the runway and obstacles may well be present at distances greater than this, in which case, large scale maps will have to be used to determine additional obstacles.

Type A Charts therefore provide information on relatively close-in obstacles and are designed to cover the take-off flight path funnel — referred to in the specific performance section — wide enough for aeroplanes with a wing span of up to 200 ft. At UK aerodromes the divergent flight path funnel is normally positioned symmetrically about the runway extended

CARDIFF

CARDIFF

AERODROME OBSTRUCTION CHART - ICAO
TYPE A - OPERATING LIMITATIONS

ELEVATIONS IN FEET
ALL OTHER DIMENSIONS IN METRES

Magnetic Variation 8°10'W (Oct 1979)

RUNWAY 13-31

DECLARED DISTANCES

	RWY 13	RWY 31
TAKE-OFF RUN •	2134	2134
EMERGENCY DISTANCE	2134	2350
TAKE-OFF DISTANCE	2195	2430
LANDING DISTANCE	2134	1981

OVERALL RUNWAY GRADIENT 1:1400

HORIZONTAL SCALE 1:10,000

FEET

METRES

METRES
FEET
VERTICAL
SCALE
1:1000

LEGEND

IDENTIFICATION No.	⊕
HEIGHT AOD	■
APPROACH LIGHT	•
AERIAL	○
TREE	•
ILS	••

AMENDMENT RECORD

No :	DATE	ENTERED BY

CIVIL AVIATION AUTHORITY 1979

11

centre-line, but provision is made in the ICAO specification to enable the charts to illustrate a turning take-
off flight path.

Availability of Type A Charts for UK aerodromes
may be ascertained by reference to the latest AIC. A
speciment Type A Chart (approximately ⅙ scale) is
shown on page 00, and it is interesting to note all the
aspects thus far discussed illustrated in the reproduc-
tion.

4.8   **Runway Surface**
The Airport and Aerodrome schedules of the AIP
describe the nature of the runway surfaces, e.g.
asphalt, concrete, grass, etc. Performance Group A
aeroplanes operate from hard, usually concrete/asphalt
surfaces, whereas aeroplanes of other performance
groups may operate out of aerodromes whose runways
consist of grass, concrete, or asphalt.

It will be seen on the specimen Type A Chart that
the 'overall gradient', or slope is given as 1:1400 =
0.07%, or, calculating in the manner described in 4.6:

> Elevation of start of R/W 13 = 205 ft.
> Elevation of start of R/W 31 = 209 ft.
> Difference = 4 ft in 2134 m.

$$\text{Thus R/W slope} = \frac{4 \times 100}{2134 \times 3.28} = \frac{400}{7000} = 0.05\%$$

In the case of R/W 13 the mean slope would therefore
be 0.05% **Uphill**, and R/W 31 0.05% **Downhill**.

It will also be seen on the specimen chart that at
approximately 1300 m from the start of R/W 31 the
runway rises 229 ft. Thus the slope value for that part
of the runway is in fact 0.47% **Uphill** — a difference of
0.52% from that previously calculated.

It can therefore be seen that, for any aeroplane of
any Performance Group expecting to use something
less than the entire runway, care and discretion
should be exercised in the selection of the slope value
to be used when determining the RTOW and V1/VR for
Performance Group A aeroplanes — since, as will be
seen, the different slope values used can significantly
affect the take-off distances required.

5. Meteorological Data

In order to comply with the AN(G)R, meteorological data relevant to the planned flight must be obtained prior to take-off, the regulations generally requiring the provision and use of the actual or reported conditions for take-off while accepting forecast conditions for the en-route and landing phases. From the aeroplane performance aspect, the most important items are Pressure Altitude, Temperature, Wind Velocity and, when conditions so require, the state or condition of the Runway Surface.

5.1 **Source(s) of data**

The UK AIP — Meteorology (CAP 32), part of the AIP — details the contents of the primary sources of the information required for the assessment of aeroplane performance, i.e. TAFs — Aerodrome Forecast; METARs — Aerodrome Reports; and short term (two hours) landing forecasts — TRENDS, which may be added to the METARs.

At certain aerodromes, information in respect of the runway state is added to the METAR when conditions so require. Amendments to TAFs are issued when forecast conditions change significantly. The documentation outlined is available to crews at self-briefing prior to flight, it being part of the documentation routinely available.

5.2 **Pressure Altitude**

Among the definitions given in JAR 1 is that for the International Standard Atmosphere (ISA), which also states that for the purpose of JAR, ISA conditions are acceptable. In terms of altitude, this means that aeroplane performance will be predicated on the use of 'the height in the standard atmosphere at which the prevailing pressure occurs' — Pressure Altitude. In Flight and Operations Manuals, wherever it appears, Altitude should be read as Pressure Altitude for performance purposes.

5.2.1   Determining Pressure Altitude

The documentation provided on departure will usually contain the aerodrome QNH — the aerodrome pressure. To convert aerodrome level to pressure altitude the following method is recommended:

(i)   Determine the difference between the aerodrome QNH and the standard setting of 1013.2 mb.

(ii)   Assuming 30 ft/mb, calculate the difference in terms of feet.

(iii)   Apply the height difference calculated in (ii) to the aerodrome elevation by adding the difference if the QNH is lower than standard, or subtracting if the QNH is higher than standard.

Table 5.1

Pressure Altitude
Correction Factors vs QNH Pressure

Pressure Altitude Correction Factor Pressure Altitude = Field Elevation ± Correction	QNH Pressure	
	mb	in
−600 ft	1034-1032	30.57-30.48
−500 ft	1031-1029	30.47-30.38
−400 ft	1028-1025	30.37-30.28
−300 ft	1024-1022	30.27-30.18
−200 ft	1021-1019	30.17-30.08
−100 ft	1018-1015	30.07-29.98
0	1014-1012	29.97-29.88
+100 ft	1011-1008	29.87-29.78
+200 ft	1007-1005	29.77-29.68
+300 ft	1004-1002	29.67-29.58
+400 ft	1001-998	29.57-29.48
+500 ft	997-995	29.47-29.38
+600 ft	994-991	29.37-29.28
+700 ft	990-988	29.27-29.18
+800 ft	987-985	29.17-29.08
+900 ft	984-981	29.07-28.98
+1000 ft	980-978	28.97-28.88
+1100 ft	977-974	28.87-28.78
+1200 ft	973-971	28.77-28.68
+1300 ft	970-968	28.67-28.58
+1400 ft	967-964	28.57-28.48
+1500 ft	963-961	28.47-28.38
+1600 ft	960-957	28.37-28.28
+1700 ft	956-954	28.27-28.18

The following example outlines the given method:

Aerodrome elevation	500 ft amsl
Aerodrome QNH	996 mb
Diff. 1013.2 — 996	+17.2 mb
	×30
	=516 ft
	+500 ft
Aerodrome pressure altitude	=1016 ft

Table 5.1 illustrates typical pressure altitude correction information that may be found in Flight and/or Operations Manuals; it incorporates the simple calculation given above. It may be that the documentation includes QNE in which case calculations or corrections will not be required, it being the aerodrome pressure altitude.

5.3 Temperature

The regulations require that performance be assessed using the actual or reported temperature for take-off, and the expected or forecast temperatures for the en-route and landing phases. Notwithstanding the statement to the contrary, made in the AIP (AGA 6-1), the en-route and landing phases may be satisfied by the use of 'Declared Temperatures', i.e. temperatures based on records which have been treated statistically.

5.3.1 Ambient Temperature

The free air statistic temperature. The normal unit used is that of degrees **Celsius**. Some American Flight Manuals may contain data in terms of Fahrenheit.

5.3.2 Declared Temperature

The accepted formula for the calculation of declared temperature is contained in the AIP — Aerodrome Temperature Data — (AGA 6-1); the appropriate mean monthly temperature, plus one-half the associated standard deviation from ISA.

Where declared temperatures are used they must be used consistently and in a conservative manner, bearing in mind that the appropriate mean monthly temperature is that which is representative of the period within which operations are expected to take place.

Declared temperatures should be considered unusable if their value is within 5°C of the maximum temperature in which satisfactory operation of the aeroplane has been established. Should the actual temperature be more than 8°C above the declared temperature, then the actual temperature should be used.

5.4   **Wind**
In order to satisfy the requirements of the AN(G)R it is necessary to use the reported, or actual wind for take-off, and the expected or forecast wind for en-route and landing phases. UK Flight Manual data for take-off and landing is based on the wind velocity as measured at a height of ten metres (33 ft) above the runway surface. Also, the Flight Manual will usually contain a wind component chart or graph for converting wind velocity into components parallel with and at right angles to the direction of the runway.

It should be borne in mind that wind directions given in the meteorological documentation are usually expressed in relation to True North, in which case local magnetic variation must be applied to the direction for comparison with the runway direction. Wind directions, as reported by ATC, are usually related to Magnetic North and, thus, do not require conversion to compare with the runway direction.

The wind component used for compliance with the regulations for take-off distances, take-off flight paths, and landing distances requires adjustment so that account is taken of **not more than 50% of a headwind component** and, **not less than 150% of a tailwind component**. Factoring the wind in this manner is to allow for the variability of the wind itself, erroneous forecasting, variations in the points of wind measurement and, in the landing case, the effects on approach speeds and landing techniques.

Some Flight Manuals may already incorporate the regulatory factorisation, most Performance Group A aeroplanes for example. Other Performance Groups may vary in terms of Manual content; personnel responsible for performance assessment should ascertain factorisation content, prior to using the Manual. Factoring the wind, as described, is not required for the en-route phase. As with pressure altitude and temperature, wind data for take-off may be obtained from the self-briefing documentation.

5.5 Runway State

The condition or state of the take-off and/or landing runway surface is appended to the METAR, when conditions so require. Included in the coded message, consisting of an eight-figure group, is the runway designator, the runway deposit (contaminant), extent of runway contamination, depth of deposit, and the friction coefficient, or braking action. The foregoing is contained in CAP 32 and is recommended reading. Runway contamination and its implications are covered in the specific performance section more fully.

SECTION TWO

6. Aeroplanes Classified In Performance Group A

6.1   The requirements of Regulation 7 and the associated airworthiness requirements of JAR 25 form the basis for providing an adequate, broad and uniform level of safety for large (exceeding 5700 kg maximum total weight authorised) multi-engined aeroplanes. In order to provide the requisite safety levels at all phases of flight, it is necessary to ensure that aeroplane performance, under assumed engine failure conditions and stipulated meteorological conditions, will be adequate at the proposed take-off weight.

Regulation 7 provides the basis on which the performance assessment is to be conducted by detailing the required performance level appropriate to the phase of flight, and by stipulating the parameters to be used. The Regulation also achieves some measure of standardisation of procedures.

6.2   **Take-off Requirements**

6.2.1   Maximum Authorised Take-off Weight
This is a structural limitation not within the bounds of the Regulation and given in the Flight Manual, and must **not** be exceeded. Some Flight Manuals may also give a 'ramp weight', the difference between the two being accounted for as taxi fuel.

6.2.2   Maximum Take-off Weight — Altitude and Temperature
Regulation 7(1) requires:

that the weight does not exceed the maximum take-off weight for altitude and temperature specified for the altitude and temperature at the aerodrome at which the take-off is to be made.

This is more commonly known as the WAT Limit — Weight, Altitude and Temperature. The WAT Limit is usually illustrated in a Flight Manual by a graph or curve and may sometimes be referred to as 'take-off climb limits' or 'second segment climb limits'. The WAT graph or curve ensures that, at the given weight, the aeroplane will have an acceptable minimum climb or acceleration capability, with all engines operating and with one engine inoperative. The minimum acceptable gradients, appropriate to the various segments of the take-off flight path are shown in Table 6.2, and the take-off flight path is shown in Figure 6.1.

Engine failure is assumed to occur on the ground and the take-off flight path (extending from the screen height of thirty-five feet at the end of take-off distance required, to a height of 1500 ft above the aerodrome), consists usually of four segments, each segment relating to a different aeroplane configuration.

The minimum acceptable climb gradients, appropriate to each segment. may be found at the references given in Table 6.2, which also gives the equivalent rate of climb for a given ground speed. The WAT graph gives the highest aeroplane weight at which the tabulated climb gradients can be met. It should be noted that, since the third segment is a level-flight segment, the tabulated gradients are of equivalent acceleration.

Figure 6.1

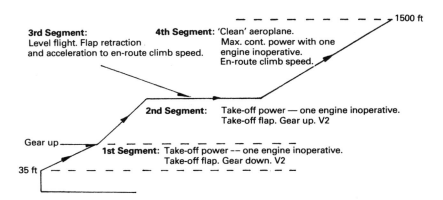

3rd Segment:
Level flight. Flap retraction and acceleration to en-route climb speed.

4th Segment: 'Clean' aeroplane.
Max. cont. power with one engine inoperative.
En-route climb speed.

1500 ft

2nd Segment: Take-off power — one engine inoperative.
Take-off flap. Gear up. V2

Gear up

1st Segment: Take-off power -- one engine inoperative.
Take-off flap. Gear down. V2

35 ft

Table 6.2

Gross Gradient of Climb (%)

(nil ground effect)

Segment	Configuration	Twin Engines	3 Engines	4 Engines	G/S kt.	Reference
1	One engine inoperative	positive	0.3 36 fpm 45 fpm	0.5 61 fpm 76 fpm	— 120 150	JAR 25 121 (a)
2	One engine inoperative	2.4 292 fpm 365 fpm	2.7 328 fpm 410 fpm	3.0 365 fpm 456 fpm	— 120 150	121 (b)
2	All engines operative	5.2 632 fpm 790 fpm	5.2 — —	5.2 — —	— 120 150	BB 119 (a)
3	One engine inoperative	1.2 146 fpm 182 fpm	1.5 182 fpm 228 fpm	1.7 207 fpm 258 fpm	— 120 150	121 (c)
4	One engine inoperative	1.2 182 fpm 219 fpm	1.5 228 fpm 273 fpm	1.7 258 fpm 310 fpm	— 150 180	121 (c)
4	All engines operative	4.0 608 fpm 730 fpm	4.0 — —	4.0 — —	— 150 180	BB 119 (b)

6.2.3 Take-off Distances

Regulation 7(2) basically requires that:

(i) the take-off run required must not exceed the take-off run available, *and*

(ii) the take-off distance required must not exceed the take-off distance available, *and*

(iii) the emergency distance required must not exceed the emergency distance available.

JAR 25, sub-parts B and BB describe the manner in which, for certification purposes, the measured performance of a Group A aeroplane is to be factored, and the take-off run, take-off distance and emergency distance required are to be scheduled in the Flight Manual. Thus, the more usual problem of matching distances available to those required provides a take-off weight dependent on the values of those distances.

6.2.4 Distances scheduled in the Flight Manual

    (i)   Take-off Run Required is the greatest of:

        (a)   1.15 times the gross distance along the take-off flight path, with all engines operating, from the start of the take-off to a point equidistant between the point at which Vlof is reached, and the point at which the aeroplane is thirty-five feet above the take-off surface.

        (b)   The gross distance along the take-off flight path from the start of the take-off to a point equidistant between the point at which Vlof is reached, and the point at which the aeroplane is thirty-five feet above the take-off surface, with the critical engine inoperative from the dry runway engine failure point.

        (c)   The gross distance along the take-off flight path from the start of the take-off to the point at which Vlof is reached, with the critical engine inoperative from the wet runway engine failure point.

Parameters (a), (b) and (c) are shown in Figures 6.3, 6.4, and 6.5, respectively.

Figure 6.3

Take-off Run Required —

All Engines Operating

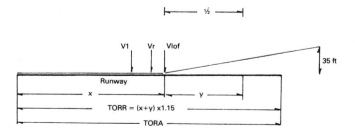

Figure 6.4

Take-off Run Required —

One Engine Inoperative

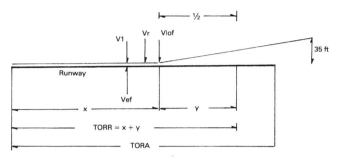

Figure 6.5

Take-off Run Required —

One Engine Inoperative (wet runway)

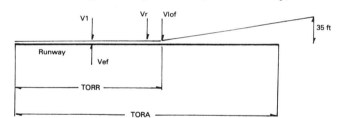

Analysis of the take-off run required, as illustrated in Figure 6.6, will show that there are two variables: aeroplane weight, and the power failure speed ratio (decision speed ratio) V1/VR. At a low weight it is possible to suffer an engine failure earlier during the take-off run than if the aeroplane is heavy, and still comply with the Regulations. Ignoring all other considerations, it may be said V1/VR; and thus V1 depends on aeroplane weight, and increases with weight. However, if all engines continue to operate during the take-off run, then an upper weight limit is imposed by the requirement of (i)(a), restricting any increase in aeroplane weight, despite the extent of the TORA.

Figure 6.6
Take-off Run Analysis

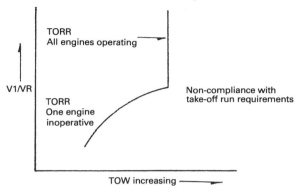

(ii) Take-off Distance Required is the greatest of:

(a) 1.15 times the gross distance along the take-off flight path, with all engines operating, from the start of the take-off to the point at which the aeroplane is thirty-five feet above the take-off surface, at a speed not less than V2.

(b) The gross distance along the take-off flight path from the start of the take-off to the point at which the aeroplane is thirty-five feet above the take-off surface, at a speed not less than V2, the critical engine having failed at the dry runway engine failure point.

(c) The gross distance along the take-off flight path from the start of the take-off to the point at which the aeroplane is fifteen feet above the take-off surface, achieved in a manner consistent with the achievement of V2 before reaching thirty-five feet above the take-off surface, the critical engine having failed at the wet runway engine failure point.

Parameters (a), (b) and (c) are shown in Figures 6.7, 6.8 and 6.9, respectively.

As in the take-off run analysis, the same two

variables are present; as is the similar constraint in respect of take-off with all engines operating, the 1.15 factor imposing an upper weight limit, regardless of the extent of TODA. A typical graph of take-off distance analysis is shown in Figure 6.10

Figure 6.7
Take-off Distance Required — All Engines Operating

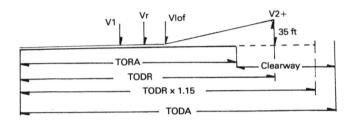

Figure 6.8
Take-off Distance Required — One Engine Inoperative

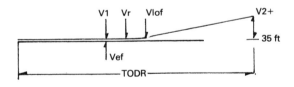

Figure 6.9
Take-off Distance Required — One Engine Inoperative (wet runway)

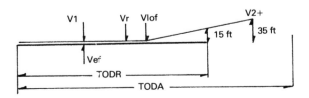

Figure 6.10
Take-off Distance Analysis

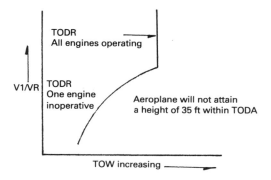

(iii) Emergency Distance Required, also termed Accelerate-stop Distance, is the greatest of:

(a) The sum of the distances necessary to accelerate the aeroplane from a standing start to Vef, corresponding to V1, for a dry runway, with all engines operating; accelerate from Vef to V1, for a dry runway; and continue the acceleration for two seconds after V1 is reached, assuming the critical engine fails at Vef; and come to a full stop on a dry hard runway from the point reached at the end of the two seconds, assuming the pilot does not apply any means of retardation until that point is reached, and that the critical engine is still inoperative.

(b) As (a), except that critical engine is assumed to fail at the wet runway engine failure point.

(c) As (a), except that all engines are operating throughout.

(d) As (b), except that all engines are operating throughout.

Parameters (a) to (d) inclusive are illustrated in Figures 6.11, 6.12 and 6.13, respectively. When analysing the emergency distance required, the same two variables are present. However, in this case as aeroplane weight increases, V1/VR will decrease, i.e. the greater the aeroplane weight, the greater the distance required to bring the aeroplane to a full stop. A typical analysis graph of emergency distance is shown in Figure 6.14.

Figure 6.11
Emergency Distance Required — One Engine Inoperative (dry)

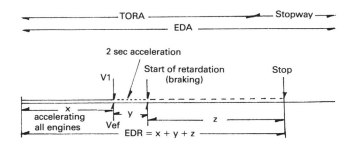

Figure 6.12
Emergency Distance Required — One Engine Inoperative (wet)

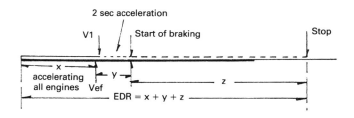

Figure 6.13
Emergency Distance Required — All engines operating

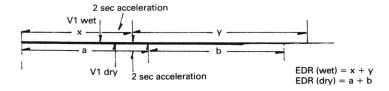

Figure 6.14
Emergency Distance Analysis

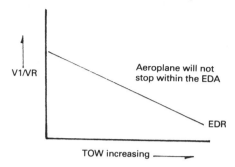

6.3   Determining Field Length Limited Take-off Weight

(i)   In addition to listing the field length requirements that must be satisfied, Regulation 7(2) also lists the operational variables to be considered with the distances available associated with the take-off runway. The operational variables are:

(a)   aeroplane weight

(b)   aerodrome pressure altitude

(c)   aerodrome temperature

(d)   runway slope

(e)   wind component: not more than 50% of a headwind component, and not less than 150% of a tailwind component

(f)   runway surface condition

The usual problem being to find the limiting value of (a) and its associated V1/VR, given (b) to (f) and the runway distances available.

(ii)   From the distance analysis graphs appropriate to 6.2.4 (i), (ii) and (iii) it may be seen that both 'all engines operating' and 'one engine inoperative' cases are satisfied, in accordance with the AN(G)R and JAR 25. The 'all engines operating' case occurs on every normal take-off, with the 1.15 factor ensuring that the probability of exceeding the scheduled take-off run or take-off distance will be remote. The 'one engine inoperative' distances are unfactored because the full distance is required only when engine failure occurs at the most critical engine failure speed; the probability of this also lies within the remote range.

(iii) For given values of (a) to (e), the 'all engines operating ' take-off run and take-off distance are constant; or, in terms of take-off weight, for given values of (b) to (e) and the field distances, the maximum take-off weight is limited by the factor of 1.15 times the gross distance being available — the maximum take-off weight will remain constant because of that factor. It is usually represented by a vertical line on an analysis graph.

'One engine inoperative' distances are a function of aeroplane weight and the speed at which engine failure occurs, or is assumed to occur. Figure 6.15 illustrates the relationship between take-off weight and V1/VR for field values of aerodrome distances and the operational variables (b) to (f). It may be noted that the diagram is in fact a composite graph of the three distance analysis graphs plotted on the same axis.

(iv) The individual characteristics of each of the curves of Figure 6.15 have been described already, but it must be realised that the relative position of each of the curves, and its shape, will depend on the aerodrome distances and operational variables used to determine each. Analysis of the figure will provide a maximum take-off weight and its associated V1/VR which will satisfy both AN(G)R and JAR. The maximum take-off weight and its associated V1/VR is determined by the **lowest** weight at which the Emergency Distance curve intercepts either of the other curves. In the case illustrated, point X is the maximum take-off weight, limited by the 'one engine inoperative' take-off distance. Thus, if the runway is dry, any combination of take-off weight and V1/VR which, when plotted on the graph, lies to the right of any of the other curves will result in exceeding at least one of the distances involved.

In Figure 6.15:

AB = weight at which the 'all engines operating' take-off distance required equals
the take-off distance available.

BC = weight/V1 relationship for the 'one
engine inoperative' take-off distance required equals the take-off distance available.

DE = weight at which the 'all engines operating' take-off run required equals the
take-off run available.

EF = weight/V1 relationship for the 'one
engine inoperative' take-off run required
equals the take-off run available.

GH = relationship of emergency distance
required equals emergency distance
available.

The relative positions of BC and EF depend on the amount of clearway available; as clearway increases, BC moves progressively to the right. It is sometimes possible, by specifying a 'maximum usable clearway', to ensure that BC never reaches a position to the right of EF, i.e. the 'one engine

Figure 6.15

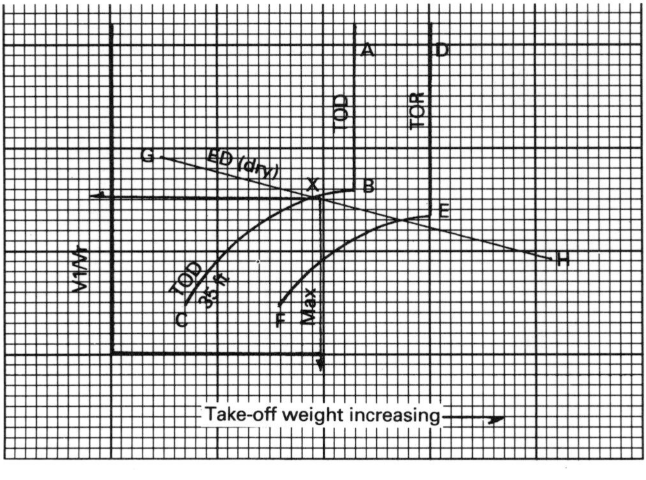

29

inoperative' take-off distance exceeding the 'one engine inoperative' take-off run. With this specification, take-off run can never be limiting.

6.4   V1/VR Range

(i)   As stated, the relative position and shape of each curve of the composite graph depends on the information used to determine it. In Figure 6.16, it is assumed that the emergency distance available has been increased from its previous value, resulting in the curve GH adopting a position KL. The maximum take-off weight obtained from this analysis (determined by the lowest weight given by the intersection of the EDA with any of the other curves) would be coincident with that appropriate to the maximum take-off weight for the 'all engines operating' take-off distance — AYB. Associated with the increase of the EDA is the fact that because of where it intersects the take-off distance curve, a V1/VR range becomes available for the maximum

Figure 6.16

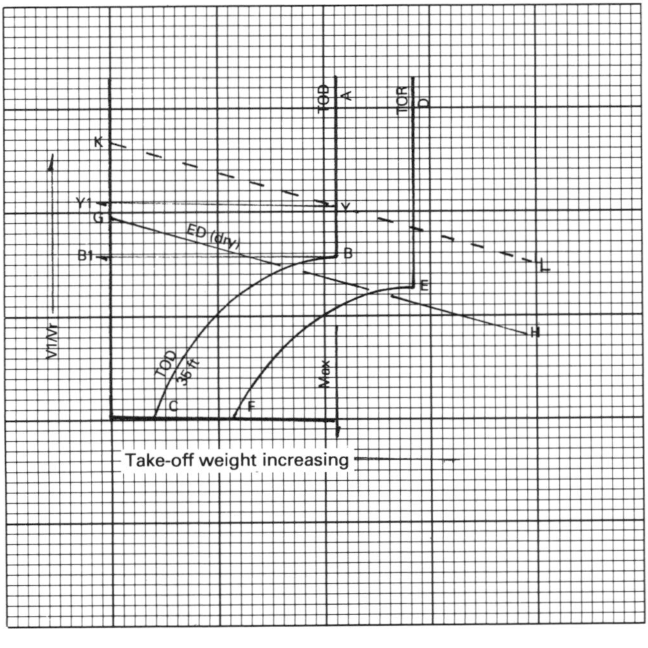

30

take-off weight: YB or Y1 to B1 which respectively, after conversion to a V1 speed, may be termed V1 High and V1 Low. This effectively means that, for both decision speeds, the aeroplane take-off performance will satisfy the stopping and the continued take-off requirements at the maximum take-off weight.

(ii) Another case whereby a V1/VR range becomes available is illustrated in Figure 6.17, when the actual take-off weight is less than the field length limited take-off weight. As can be seen in the diagram, the actual take-off weight intersects the EDA curve at N and the 'one engine inoperative' curve at M, giving a V1/VR range of N1 to M1.

(iii) A third occasion when a V1/VR range becomes available is when the aeroplane is WAT limited. Referring again to Figure 6.17, it can be seen that, if the actual take-off weight is substituted by the WAT limited weight, an identical situation to (ii) would exist.

It may be deduced from the illustrations dealing with a V1/VR range that the extent of the range available will be dependent on the difference between the actual or, in the latter case, the WAT limited weight and the field length limited weight, i.e. as the difference increases so does

Figure 6.17

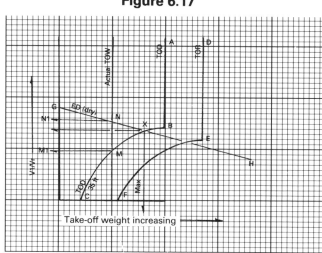

the extent of the range available. It should also be apparent that should the WAT limited weight coincide with the field length limit, then no range would exist. Also, should the WAT limited weight increase so that its curve lay to the right of the field length limit, then the field length limited weight would prevail.

Therefore a V1/VR range becomes available when:

(i)   The actual take-off weight is exceeded by the field length limited weight and/or the WAT limited weight.

(ii)   The WAT limited take-off weight is exceeded by the field length limited take-off weight.

(iii)   The maximum permitted take-off weight is limited by the 'all engines operating' take-off distance required.

(iv)   The maximum authorised take-off weight is exceeded by the field length limited take-off weight and/or the WAT limited take-off weight.

It must be noted that, in all cases where a range of decision speeds becomes available, the use of a V1 exceeding the value of the V1 High calculated may result in exceeding the emergency distance available, assuming the engine failure occurs at the used V1; use of a V1 lower than that calculated may result in the aeroplane not reaching the required screen height of thirty-five feet at V2, again assuming engine failure occurred at the used V1. Selection and use of the appropriate decision speed would depend on company procedures and/or operational factors.

6.5   **Wet Runways**
The take-off field length requirements, outlined in 6.2, include accountability for wet runways where reduced wheel braking capability on a wet runway of defined friction characteristics is used to obtain a wet V1/VR. In Figure 6.18 KL represents the weight — V1/VR relationship for emergency distance required equal to emergency distance available. The maximum take-off weight moves from X to Z, which represents quite a severe reduction in take-off weight. Consequently, the requirements were modified on the basis of a marked

improvement in safety for the abandoned take-off on a wet runway, in exchange for a relatively small degradation in safety for the continued take-off, using a wet V1/VR. Thus the requirements allowed for:

(a) a reduction in screen height at the end of the take-off distance to not less than fifteen feet, and

(b) lift-off at the end of the take-off run available.

In the case illustrated in Figure 6.18, this gives a maximum take-off weight and V1/VR corresponding to S, which is slightly higher than X, the dry runway limiting weight. Therefore, the limiting weight would remain at X, but the V1/VR would be read at R, resulting in a screen height at the end of the take-off distance of approximately eighteen feet (by interpolation).

Figure 6.18

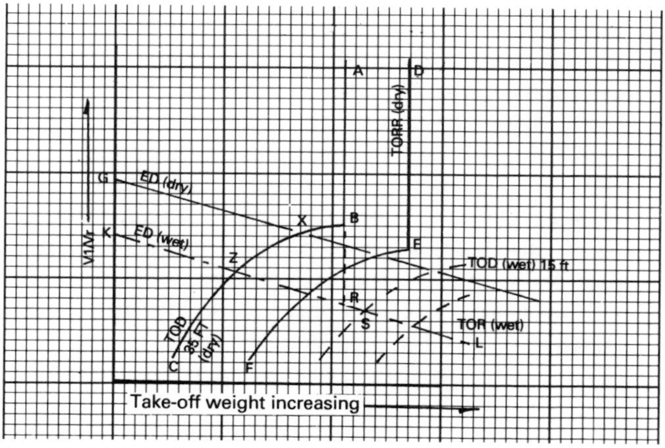

6.6 Balanced Field Length (BFL)

A simple solution to the problem of calculating the field length limited take-off weight is provided by the use of the BFL concept which assumes that EDA is equal to TODA.

Developed from the individual graphs to constitute a BFL Chart, or Generalised Take-off chart, it will provide a pre-computed solution for point X — the field length limited take-off weight; in such a situation with two of the field lengths being equal, the take-off run requirement should not be limiting, the weight obtained from the chart will be the limiting take-off weight, provided that the 'all engines operating' take-off distance is not limiting. Therefore, when using a BFL or Generalised Take-off Chart, it is necessary to check the 'all engines operating' take off distance, unless the Flight Manual indicates that this has been incorporated already. It should be understood, that if clearway exists to the extent that TODA actually exceeds EDA, and the BFL charts are used to determine the maximum take-off weight, an aeroplane weight penalty will be incurred. When using a BFL chart for twin-engined operations, it may be found that the limiting factor is usually the 'one engine inoperative' case, but the BFL assumption provides a ready means of determining the field length limited take-off weight and its associated V1/VR.

6.7 **Contaminated Runways**

The AN(G)R requires all Group A aeroplanes' performance to account for the condition of the runway surface — 7(2) (d) — when determining the field length limited take-off weight. This refers to operations from runways contaminated by snow, slush, ice or water; the main concern being the inadequacy of friction between the aeroplane tyres and the runway surface, particularly when take-off and landing speeds are as high as is the case with turbo-jet transport aeroplanes current at the time of writing, because the stopping performance of these aeroplanes is mainly dependent on the friction available; and, in some cases, the runway length(s) required for take-off and landing may be critical in relation to the lengths available.

The main problems arising from operations on contaminated runways are:

(a) Deterioration of performance in both acceleration and braking, the former due to drag caused by contaminant impact on the airframe which is caused by spray from the main wheels; the latter due to decreased friction between the tyres and the runway surface.

(b) Directional control problems due to decreased friction affecting nose-wheel steering and differential and normal wheel braking.

(c) Impact damage caused by the spray sent up by both the nose wheel and main wheels, affecting the leading edges, main gear assembly, flaps and tail section.

(d) Engine combustion problems caused by spray ingestion, especially with rear (tail) mounted engines.

Thus it is essential that adequate information concerning runway friction characteristics and braking action is made available to the pilot so that he/she can adjust operating techniques and apply performance corrections.

This information is required for three distinct purposes:

(i) Deceleration after landing, or a rejected take-off

(ii) maintenance of directional control during the ground roll on take-off and landing, especially with a cross-wind, asymmetric engine power or technical malfunction; and

(iii) wheel spin-up at touch-down on landing.

In relation to braking or directional control, runway friction plays a vital role when considering the factors which may impair braking action, induced by various human and/or technical anomalies. All aeroplanes are subject to specific cross-wind limitations; these limits, in terms of cross-wind components, decreasing with runway surface friction. Wheel spin-up may be significantly affected by the lack of surface friction as, at touch-down on landing, the wheels must attain maximum rotational speed for optimum anti-skid operation and, equally important, deployment of auto-spoilers, which destroy much of the residual lift.

6.7.1 Hydroplaning

When considering a wet or water covered runway, separate but related aspects of the braking problem arise. First, there is the normal wet friction condition, whereby the presence of water on the runway reduces the available friction coefficient, caused by the water not being 'squeezed' completely from between the tyre and the runway; consequently, there is a marked reduction in the force opposing the relative motion of the tyre on the runway. It is, therefore, necessary to displace, or break through the water film in order to achieve a relatively high coefficient of friction.

A contributory factor to the displacement of the water is the aeroplane's speed: as speed increases, the time of tyre contact with the ground is reduced, thus there is less time for the process to be completed. Therefore, on wet surfaces, friction coefficient decreases as speed increases.

The factor which causes most concern in these conditions is the phenomenon of Hydroplaning or Aquaplaning, whereby contact between the tyre and the runway surface is lost, the wheel's normal load being supported by the fluid pressure of the film of water beneath the tyre. When this happens the wheel rapidly spins down, frictional forces are much reduced, and directional control may become ineffective. There are three main types of hydroplaning known to occur:

    (i)   Viscous Hydroplaning.

           This can cause a loss of friction at relatively low speeds, due to the effect of viscosity preventing the water from escaping from under the tyre. It occurs on very smooth surfaces with areas that have become heavily coated with rubber deposits (usually caused during wheel spin-up at touch-down on landing), or those areas which have become polished through traffic use. It is associated with damp/wet runways, and once initiated can persist to very low speeds. It can occur also during braking on a rejected take-off or landing roll.

    (ii)   Dynamic Hydroplaning.

           This type occurs beyond a critical speed, and is directly related to tyre pressure. The condition is due mainly to the inertial effect of water where the inflation pressure of the tyre is insufficient to displace the water from beneath the tyres during the relatively short time of contact with the surface; the condition is also associated with water coverage of a measurable depth. Generally, the higher the tyre pressure, the higher the speed at which dynamic hydroplaning will occur. It may also be experienced during the higher speeds of landing and the take-off ground roll, with as little as one millimetre of standing water sufficient to support hydroplaning. Since it is directly related to tyre pressure, a 'rule of thumb' formula may be used to assess hydroplaning speed (Vp):

$$Vp = 9. \sqrt{\text{tyre pressure (psi)}}$$

(iii) Reverted Rubber.
Present thinking related to this type of hydro-planing indicates that super-heated steam is generated between the tyre and the runway surface, resulting in melted rubber acting as a sealing agent, preventing the escape of the high pressure steam. This type of hydroplaning can develop in any situation and at any speed where the tyre is non-rotating for a prolonged period of time. Avoidance of wheel lock-up appears to be the main preventative measure.

6.7.2 Operations from Contaminated Runways
Operations from runways contaminated by snow, slush, ice and/or water, by any class of aeroplane should be avoided whenever possible. However, where such an operation is intended, it is important that the pilot is aware of the risks involved, the procedures to be used, the operating techniques to be adopted and the perform-ance corrections to be applied.

6.7.3 Reporting Runway Conditions
The method by which the runway surface condition is reported is described in the Air Pilot, AGA 9, the UK Snow Plan. The depth of snow or slush is measured at approximately 300-metre intervals, between five and ten metres from the runway centreline and clear of rutting effects. The depth is reported in millimetres (mm) for each third of the runway, and an assessment is made of the nature of the contaminant on the following scale:

Dry Snow	less than 0.35 specific gravity (SG)
Wet Snow	0.35 — 0.50 SG
Compacted Snow	over 0.50 SG
Slush	0.50 — 0.80 SG
Standing Water	1.0 SG

The presence of water on the runway will be reported as follows:

Damp	the surface shows a change of colour due to moisture.
Wet	the surface is soaked but no sig-nificant patches of standing water are visible.

Water Patches	significant patches of standing water are visible.
Flooded	extensive patches of standing water are visible.

6.7.4 Effects on Performance

Depths greater than 3 mm of water, slush or wet snow, or 10 mm of dry snow, are likely to have significant effects on performance (see 6.7). A water depth of less than 3 mm will require no corrections to take-off performance, other than the allowance applicable for the effect of a wet or slippery runway. However, when the depth varies over a runway, and when the general depth is less than 3 mm (thus insignificant effects of additional drag), pilots should be aware that there could be patches of standing water or slush of depths in excess of 15 mm during the latter part of the take-off run, which could cause ingestion, resulting in power fluctuations which could compromise safety.

In assessing the effect of increased drag, the condition of the up-wind half of the runway — the area where the aeroplane is travelling at high speed and accelerating — is most important; small isolated patches of contaminant may have a negligible effect, but if extensive areas of contaminant are present and there is doubt concerning the depth, the take-off should **not** be attempted.

Because of the great difficulty in measuring, or predicting the actual coefficient of friction, or value of displacement and impingement drag associated with contaminated runways, aeroplane performance cannot be detailed accurately; any data concerning contaminated runways contained in the Flight Manual can be regarded only as the best data available. It should be understood clearly, that in the event of engine failure during the take-off run, all classes of aeroplanes may not have the ability to continue the take-off or stop safely within the remaining distance available.

The duration of any risk period that may exist is variable and difficult to assess because of the lack of knowledge of accelerating or stopping performance associated with the various contaminants. Some reduction of risk, in a particular set of circumstances, may be achieved by a reduction in take-off weight, nevertheless **the use of a contaminated runway should be avoided if**

possible. A short delay in departure, or a short hold (if possible) prior to landing may well be sufficient to remove at least some of the risks.

6.7.5 Take-off Procedures

When operations from contaminated runways are unavoidable, the following suggested procedures may assist in enhancing the safety aspect of the operation:

(a) **Take-off should not be attempted** in depths of dry snow greater than 60 mm; or water, slush and wet snow greater than 15 mm. If the snow is very dry, depth limit may be increased to 80 mm.

(b) Check the tyres are in good condition and that all retardation devices, including the anti-skid system, are fully serviceable.

(c) When considering the flap/slat configuration from the range permitted, be aware that greater increments of flaps/slats, whilst reducing the unstick speed, may well increase the effect of impingement drag. Appropriate field corrections should be applied.

(d) Ensure that de-icing of the airframe and engine intakes is carried out in the correct manner, leaving the aeroplane aerodynamically clean for take-off.

(e) Do not carry unnecessary amounts of fuel.

(f) Engine and airframe anti-icing drills and procedures should be strictly adhered to.

(g) Do not take-off with a tailwind or, with doubtful runway conditions, in cross-winds exceeding the cross-wind limit.

(h) Use the maximum runway distance available; any significant loss of distance incurred during the line-up process should be deducted from the declared distance to re-calculate the maximum take-off weight for the prevailing conditions.

(i) Normal speed schedules should be used. Any procedure involving the use of overspeed techniques, or the use of reduced thrust for take-off should **not** be used.

(j)   Pilots should consider the nature of the over-run area and the consequences of use thereof for the particular runway; also, weather changes, especially precipitation and temperature since the last braking and/or runway report, and the effect on performance, and whether or not subsequent depths exceed limitations.

The CAA Airworthiness Division of the Safety Regulation Group will advise on the safety aspect of any proposed changes to normal procedures or to those listed above.

6.7.6   Take-off Performance

Most Flight Manuals contain limitations and performance corrections expressed in Water Equivalent Depth — WED — (WED = Depth × SG). However, WED values are not available to pilots, therefore operators present limitations and performance corrections in the form of reported precipitation depths in their Operations Manuals. The limiting depths and the SG values given in 6.7.3 should be assumed.

It follows from the preceding paragraphs that the take-off weight appropriate to a contaminated runway should not exceed that permitted for a dry runway. If a normal take-off weight analysis results in an obstacle limited take-off weight, it is necessary to assume, for the contaminated runway, that TODA = TOD required for the dry runway obstacle limited take-off weight.

Performance data for contaminated runways given in most Flight Manuals assumes that, for take-off, all engines are operating. Safety margins, which are provided on a normal take off to take account of engine failure, are therefore not available in the case of a contaminated runway.

Most Flight Manuals also contain advisory information relating to the determination of a maximum speed for abandoning a take-off on a contaminated runway. This speed (Vstop) is an approximation to the maximum speed from which a safe stop may be made, with all engines operating. It is **not** a V1, since it implies no capability of continuing the take-off in the event of engine failure, and, unlike V1, it could be less than Vmcg.

For further information concerning the risks and factors associated with operations from contaminated runways, the reader should refer to AIC 82/1986.

6.8 Constraints on V1

Before calculating the maximum permitted take-off weight (ignoring obstacle clearance, en-route and landing requirements), there are constraints on V1 which may necessitate a reduction in the calculated take-off weight. These constraints are:

(a) V1 must never be less than Vmcg.

(b) V1 must never exceed Vmbe.

(c) V1 must never exceed VR.

6.9 Other Airworthiness Constraints

As well as the constraints listed in 6.8, airworthiness limitations (such as tyre speed, brake energy capacity, and minimum 'quick turn-round time') should be considered since any one of these may cause a reduction in take-off weight:

(i) The speed rating of the aeroplane's tyres will be specified in the Flight Manual, which will also contain data appropriate to that rating for given conditions of pressure altitude, ambient temperature and wind component, enabling the maximum take-off weight the tyres can sustain to be calculated.

Usually, under normal operating conditions, tyre speed limitation is unrestrictive. However, under conditions of a hot, high-altitude aerodrome with an appreciable tailwind component for take-off, it may be found that tyre speed limits are a restricting factor in terms of take-off weight.

(ii) Although brake design allows for enormous energy absorption (especially in the case of a rejected take-off at a high weight), even the brake units have a limit above which brake fading or failure may occur. The amount of energy the brakes can sustain is affected mainly by aeroplane weight and is given in terms of a maximum speed for that weight; so that, in the event of a rejected take-off at that speed, the aeroplane may be brought to a safe stop, within the brakes' energy capacity and the stipulated or regulatory criteria. As with the tyre speed limit, brake energy capacity is affected by pressure altitude, ambient temperature, runway slope, and wind component, relative to the take-off runway; also, it is adversely affected by hot, high-altitude aerodromes whose take-off runways have a down slope and a tailwind component. Should the brake energy speed (Vmbe) be less than V1 for a given weight, a reduction in V1, a reduction in take-off weight, or possibly a combination of both may be sought.

6.10 Summary

It must appear to be a daunting task, to relate the distances given in 6.2 in terms of the variables given in 6.3 (b) to (f). In practice, the process is carried out prior to the data being scheduled in the Flight Manual; only the limiting values of the distances involved are given, the Flight Manual presenting a relatively simple, graphical solution for obtaining the field length limited take-off weight.

Presentation of performance data may vary among aeroplane types, but CAP 385 (Specimen Performance Charts) is considered to be fairly representative of Group A aeroplanes. Data contained in the Flight Manual should normally incorporate the factored field lengths and wind components, but this should be checked before use.

Operations from contaminated runways are usually covered in an advisory form. However, data must be determined and included for calculating Vstop in conditions of very low braking coefficients of friction. If take-off is to be made under such conditions, be aware of the implications involved and the procedures to be used, and 'if in doubt, do not take-off'.

The effects on take-off weight of obstacle clearance, en-route, and landing requirements have yet to be considered. Optional procedures (for example, reduced take-off thrust), and increased V2 procedure are discussed in the appendices.

Obstacle Clearance

6.11   In order to satisfy the requirements of Regulation 7(3), it is necessary to show (using the aeroplane's Flight Manual and the data referring to the 'one engine inoperative' net take-off flight path (NTOFP)), that in the vertical plane, the net flight path will clear all obstacles by not less than thirty-five feet. Provision is made for a turn but, if the change of direction exceeds fifteen degrees, the vertical clearance is increased to fifty feet, with the radius of turn not less than that specified in the Flight Manual.

To calculate the net flight path, net climb performance must be used; the net climb gradients used being the gross climb gradients, reduced by the following margins:

Twin-engined aeroplane (one engine inoperative): 0.8%
Three-engined aeroplane (one engine inoperative):0.9%
Four-engined aeroplane (one engine inoperative): 1.0%

These margins represent a very low probability factor (1×10^{-1}), the low levels of clearance being acceptable only in the rare event of continuing a take-off, following engine failure, so close to V1 that there is negligible 'all engines' benefit from a delayed engine failure. The probability of this is remote (1×10^{-6}), thus the probability of attaining net performance after engine failure is about 1×10^{-7}; referring to Table 1.1, it will be seen this lies within the remote range. To achieve the same level of probability in the absence of engine failure, 1×10^{-7} equates to a 3.2% climb gradient margin.

6.12   **The Take-off Flight Path Area**
AN(G)R 7(3) (b) (i) and (ii) define the dimensions of the area within which obstacles must be considered, and can be summarised as:

Configuration	Semi-width at origin	Divergence	Max. Semi-width
One engine inoperative	60m+wing span/2	Distance/8	900 m

A plan view of this is shown in Figure 6.19, the area being more commonly known as the take-off 'funnel', which originates at the end of the take-off distance available and is used for identifying obstacles.

6.13   The Take-off Flight Path

The take-off flight path is the true height versus distance relationship assuming failure of the critical engine during take-off. Properly termed the Net Take-off Flight Path, it is divided into segments, defined by changes in aeroplane configuration, engine thrust, or aeroplane speed.

The NTOFP profile is shown in Figure 6.1, and the segment-related climb gradient requirements are shown in Table 6.2; both can be compared with Figure 6.20 which shows a composite picture of the flight path, the funnel, and the thirty-five-foot clearance required throughout. It should be understood that the expanding funnel is coincident with the take-off flight path only when the take-off distance required equals the take-off distance available; also, remember that the funnel is used for obstacle identification, whereas the flight path is used for obstacle clearance. An important position in the NTOFP is that known as 'reference zero'; it is defined as 'the point on the ground thirty-five feet immediately below the aeroplane, at the end of take-off distance **required**'; it is the reference to which the co-ordinates of the various points in the flight path are referred and is the point at which (thirty-five feet above) the NTOFP starts, through the various segments and ending 1500 ft above the aerodrome level, unless obstacle height requires a further extension.

The variables to be taken into account when determining the NTOFP and the clearance by thirty-five feet of all obstacles therein are:

(a)   Aeroplane weight at the start of take-off

(b)   Aerodrome pressure altitude

(c)   Aerodrome ambient temperature

(d)   Wind component

(e)   The obstacle chartacteristics in relation to the take-off distance available.

Although the form of the NTOFP may usually be similar to that shown in Figures 6.1 and 6.20, other options are possible and/or necessary. For example, a turn or turns may be required below 1500 ft; flaps may be scheduled at a maximum level-off height; or a second-segment extended V2 climb may be required. These variations are dealt with in the appendices.

Figure 6.19
The Take-off Flight Path 'Funnel'

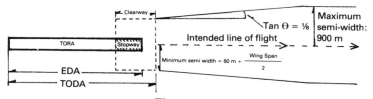

Figure 6.20
The Net Take-off Flight Path

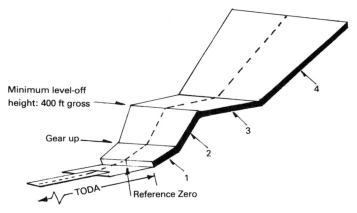

6.13.1 Assumed Climb Technique

As previously stated, the flight path begins at reference zero where the aeroplane has attained a height of thirty-five feet at V2, assuming failure of the critical engine at V1. Landing gear retraction is completed at the end of the first segment, and the climb is continued at V2, with flaps at the take-off setting, using take-off thrust until:

(i) a minimum gross height of 400 ft is attained, or

(ii) the maximum level-off height is attained, or

(iii) the maximum height which can be attained within the take-off thrust time limit has been reached. The time limit (usually five minutes) is normally taken from brake release at take-off.

6.13.2   Turns
The aeroplane may make a turn to avoid limiting obstacles provided the requirements outlined in 6.7.10 are complied with. Turns in the NTOFP are usually restricted to the second and fourth segments, as climb data for the first and third segments cannot be accurately determined, due to changing aeroplane configuration and/or acceleration.

Where a turn is required, the procedure should be adequately detailed in the Company Operations Manual, and the point at which to start the turn should be readily identifiable by the pilot, when flying on instruments (obstacle clearance on a 'see and avoid' basis in **not** permitted). Standard Instrument Departures (SID) requiring a turn or turns below 1500 ft should be checked for obstacle clearance. Where detailed obstacle data for SID is not available, the operator should ascertain that the obstacle profile along the SID is not worse than the profile given on the Type A Chart for a straight ahead departure. A plan view of a turning flight path and its associated funnel is shown in Figure 6.21.

6.13.3   Maximum Level-off Height (MLOH)
Clearance of relatively close-in obstacles may be achieved by delaying flap retraction, until above the normal minimum of 400 ft. However, depending on the climb gradient for the take-off weight, the second segment height may be limited; this is the maximum level-off height. If V2 climb is terminated at MLOH, acceleration to final-segment climb speed within the take-off power time limit is guaranteed.

6.13.4   Obstacle in the Third Segment
An obstacle in the third segment must be cleared at or before the end of the second segment; this may be limited by the maximim level-off height.

6.13.5   Extended V2 climb (second segment)
An obstacle cleared on this basis must be the last obstacle in the take-off flight path. Provided the aeroplane has a minimum acceleration/climb gradient at all points in the flight path above 400 ft, as given in the Flight Manual, when using maximum continuous

thrust, the maximum level-off height no longer limits the height at which the second-segment climb at V2 must be terminated. Instead, the V2 climb may be continued until the thrust time-limit is reached.

Figure 6.21

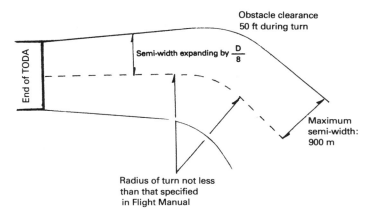

6.14 Effect of Runway Slope on Obstacle Characteristics

Although not included in the operational variables to be taken into account when determining the NTOFP, the slope of the take-off surfaces affects the NTOFP in relation to the obstacle and, consequently, the obstacle limited take-off weight. Obstacle characteristics i.e. height and distance, are generally referred to the elevation of the end of TODA, whereas the NTOFP is referred to 'reference zero'. Therefore, in order to position the obstacle in relation to the NTOFP, a relationship between the obstacle characteristics and reference zero has to be established. Figures 6.22 (a), (b) and (c) illustrate the take-off flight paths for level, up-sloping and down-sloping take-off distances, respectively. In each case, Flight Path 1 uses the entire TODA; whilst Flight Path 2, due to decreased weight, uses something less, annotated TODR 1 and TODR 2, respectively. It is assumed that the climb gradients for both flight paths are the same.

(i) Level take-off Distance
In Figure 6.22 (a), it can be seen that the take-off distance required by Flight Path 2 (TODR 2) has decreased, in comparison to Flight Path 1

(TODR 1). It may also be seen, that as a consequence, the horizontal distance (horizontal distance 2) of the obstacle from reference zero has increased; also that, since the take-off distance is level, both flight paths start at the same relative heights, thus the height of the obstacle in relation to either flight path remains unchanged.

(ii) Sloped Take-off Distance

Figure 6.22 (b) illustrates the take-off distance sloping upwards. Similar to (1) above, when weight is decreased, the take-off distance required decreases, thus the horizontal distance of the obstacle from reference zero increases, the difference being TODR 1 minus TODR 2. Since the take-off distance is sloping up, the start of Flight Path 2 occurs earlier and is thus relatively lower than the start of Flight Path 1, the difference being shown as D in the diagram,

Figure 6.22 (a)

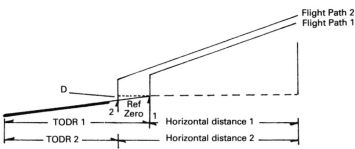

Figure 6.22 (b)

and has the effect of increasing the relative height of the obstacle by the same amount as D.

Figure 6.22 (c) illustrates the case of a down-sloping take-off distance and, as can be seen, has the effect of decreasing the obstacle's relative height.

Figure 6.22 (c)

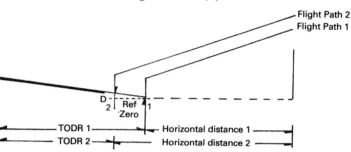

The amount D by which the relative height of the obstacle is increased or decreased can be determined as shown in Figure 6.23.

Figure 6.23

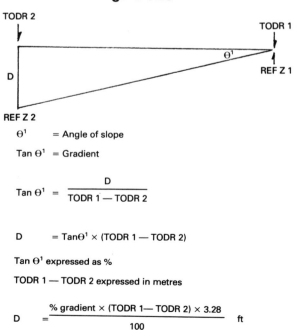

θ^1 = Angle of slope

$\tan \theta^1$ = Gradient

$$\tan \theta^1 = \frac{D}{\text{TODR 1} - \text{TODR 2}}$$

D   = $\tan \theta^1 \times$ (TODR 1 — TODR 2)

$\tan \theta^1$ expressed as %

TODR 1 — TODR 2 expressed in metres

$$D = \frac{\% \text{ gradient} \times (\text{TODR 1} - \text{TODR 2}) \times 3.28}{100} \quad \text{ft}$$

49

6.15   **Determining Obstacle Clearance**
Having determined the field length limited take-off weight, it must now be determined if, at the weight found, the aeroplane will clear all obstacles along the intended line of flight by the required thirty-five feet (or fifty feet in a turn). First, the obstacle is identified in relation to the funnel, the dimensions of which may be calculated as:

Semi-width of funnel = 60 m + wing span/2 + Distance/8

(where distance = distance of obstacle from the end of TODA).

e.g. Distance = 6000 m. Wing span = 48 m.

Thus:

Semi-width = 60 m + 24 m + 6000/8 = 84+ 750
          = 834 m.
Maximum semi-width = 900 m.

Thus an obstacle 6000 m from the end of TODA, and 800 m from the intended line of flight, would be within the funnel boundary and therefore significant.

The next step is to determine the 'one engine inoperative' NTOFP appropriate to the weight initially found. The construction of the NTOFP should start at the reference zero appropriate to the more critical take-off distance required in either of the 'one engine inoperative', and 'all engines operating' cases. Should the take-off distance required be less than TODA, then reference zero needs to be re-defined and the obstacle distance adjusted, as outlined previously. Should the take-off distance include a slope, obstacle height will also require correction. Construction of the flight path may be carried out by using the following formula (the same units must be used — feet or metres):

$$\text{Horizontal distance (HD)} = \frac{\text{change in height (ft)} \times 100}{\text{climb gradient (\%)}}$$

Correction for wind component may be made as follows:

$$\text{Corrected distance} = \frac{\text{calculated distance} \times \text{G/S}}{\text{TAS}}$$

(G/S = TAS +/− factored wind component.)

The climb gradients appropriate to individual segments may be obtained from the Flight Manual. Obstacle location and height are both compared with the NTOFP to ascertain clearance, and if the desired clearance is not obtained, then, generally, weight should be reduced; re-calculation of the NTOFP will be necessary until the required clearance, consistent with take-off weight, is achieved.

6.16 **Flight Manual Data**

It may appear from the foregoing that the calculation of an obstacle limited take-off weight is achieved by a graphical construction of the NTOFP, followed by a comparison with the obstacle characteristics. Whilst this is possible, it is lengthy and rendered unnecessary by the obstacle data contained in most Flight Manuals in the form of Obstacle Clearance Charts (graphs), which are included with obstacle characteristics in relation to reference zero, adjusted for wind component (already factored) and the gross gradient available at the given, or found, take-off weight. The resulting net height (also gross height) is compared then with the obstacle clearance height. Should the net height obtained be insufficient for obstacle clearance then, by use of the chart incorporating performances changes due to weight change, a climb gradient appropriate to obstacle clearance is found which, in turn, is related to a specific take-off weight. In effect, the NTOFP is calculated without the need to construct it.

The charts also allow for various flight path options which may be required for obstacle clearance, by including maximum level-off height and take-off thrust time limit parameters, with gross height data for determining aeroplane configuration changes. Allowance for fuel burn-off is incorporated into the charts, allowing for entry with the take-off weight, aerodrome pressure altitude and temperature where these are variable inputs. Flight Manual data may vary among aeroplane types but it is considered that the current CAP 385 is fairly representative of most Flight Manuals of Performance Group A aeroplanes; a study of the obstacle clearance charts contained in the CAP is recommended. Problems dealing with obstacle clearance and the various options are discussed in the appendices.

En-Route Requirements

6.17   The en-route phase of performance assessment concerns that portion of the flight which starts 1500 ft
above the departure aerodrome — the end of the take-
off flight path — and ends 1500 ft above the destination
or alternate aerodrome. The requirements are given in
AN(G)R 7(4) and (5), being appropriate to the 'one
engine inoperative' and 'two engines inoperative'
cases, respectively. The object of the en-route requirements is to ensure that engine failure en-route is a
surviveable incident. A single-engine failure is reason-
ably probable, whilst the probability of a second
engine failure depends, to some extent, on the number
of engines and the time elapsed since the first failure;
thus it would seem that, on a twin-engined aeroplane,
the probability of a second engine failure must be
made exteremly remote.

6.18   **Net Performance**
En-route performance following an engine failure must
be assessed using the en-route gradient of climb, or,
where scheduled, the en-route net flight path, with one
or two engines inoperative, as appropriate. Flight
Manual net data is the gross data reduced by the
following climb gradients:

Table 6.24

Aeroplane type	one engine inoperative	two engines inoperative
Twin-engined	1.1%	—
Three-engined	1.4%	0.3%
Four-engined	1.6%	0.5%

Account must be taken of the expected and forecast
meteorological conditions, including ambient temperature and, if appropriate, the aeroplane's ice protection
system may be assumed to be in use.

6.19   **One Engine Inoperative**
AN(G)R 7(4) requires that, after a single-engine failure,
the aeroplane can, using maximum continuous power

on the operating engine(s), continue the flight to an aerodrome where a safe landing may be made. The aeroplane must be capable of clearing all obstacles within ten nautical miles, either side of the intended track, by at least 2000 ft. On arrival over the aerodrome, for which the landing distance requirements have been established, the gradient of the specified flight path should not be less than zero at 1500 ft above the aerodrome.

6.20 **Two Engines Inoperative**
AN(G)R 7(5) is the regulation for 'two engines inoperative', all the requirements therein being similar to AN(G)R 7(4). However, 7(5) needs to be considered only when the aeroplane is more than ninety minutes' still air flying time from an aerodrome, for which landing distance requirements have been established. The 'ninety minutes' flying time is taken to be at the 'all engines operating' economical cruising speed, as given in the Flight Manual; it is often referred to as the 'over water speed', a misnomer since it does not relate to flight over water only. This requirement imposes a route limitation on twin-engined aeroplanes, and on aeroplanes with more than two engines which cannot maintain height following a double engine failure. Twin-engined aeroplanes should not operate on routes where, at any time, they are more than the stipulated ninety minutes from a suitable aerodrome for landing, otherwise, the risk of double engine failure becomes no longer remote — see extended twin operations (ETOPS — Appendix 1).

The effect of the requirement is to deter operators from entering into a situation where a potential double-engine failure might occur on any sector of up to three hours, or on any sector provided the aeroplane is always within ninety minutes of a suitable aerodrome. On such sectors the probability of a double-engine failure is small enough to be ignored when the aeroplane is required by the operators' rules to return to base after an early failure of one engine. There is no immediate improvement in safety levels when the time from a diversion aerodrome changes from more to less than ninety minutes, thus, the planning of longer routes merely to remain within the critical time of ninety minutes, in order to avoid the necessity of considering a double-engine failure, should be discouraged.

6.21   Drift-down

In both a single- or double-engine failure, where a drift-down procedure is assumed, the maximum height to be assumed for the start of the drift-down is the maximum re-lighting altitude, applicable to engine operation, as given in the Flight Manual. This is predicated on the assumption that first attempts to re-light the engine would result in a descent to the top of the re-light envelope, which would be unlikely to be carried out at the optimum drift-down procedure; thus the first part of the descent to the maximum re-light altitude is discounted. A drift-down may be defined as a descent from the maximum re-lighting altitude to a lower stabilising altitude, made with the operating engine(s) set at maximum continuous power, at the prescribed en-route climb speed.

AN(G)R (2) states, that credit may be taken for weight reduction in the form of jettisoning, in order to attain a relatively high stabilising altitude.

CAP 360 — Air Operators Certificates — contains information on requirements to be met by applicants and holders of these certificates, and advises operators that they should be aware of these routes where the en-route performance of their aeroplanes, following single- or double-engine failure, would be critical. Operators should include instructions relating to such routes in their Operations Manuals, so that risks which could arise from indecision or error can be reduced. On critical routes, it may, in some cases, be possible to regulate the planned take-off weight so that drift-down performance will enable the aeroplane to clear all obstacles on its route by the required margin, regardless of the point at which engine failure occurs. In other cases it may be necessary to determine a critical point, or points, at which specific action should be taken, in the event of engine failure.

The instructions should also take into account the accuracy of navigation expected of the flight crew, given the crew complement and navigation aids available. Account should also be taken of the effect of variable meteorological conditions; assumed winds and temperatures used to determine critical point(s) may well differ from actual conditions, requiring the drift-down procedure to be modified.

6.21.1 Calculating Drift-down

Since the probability of engine failure, the presence of significant obstructions, and inadequate navigation aids all occurring simultaneously is somewhat low, specific accountability for a drift-down is not included in the AN(G)R.

The maximum permissible altitude at which drift-down is assumed to start is the lower of:

(i)   the maximum re-light altitude

(ii) the planned or actual flight altitude.

Using net gradient climb data, the drift-down may be plotted as in the case of the NTOFP (distance versus height), and the required clearance checked in relation to obstructions along the drift-down route. Table 6.25 illustrates a typical format used for calculating drift-down, with two engines inoperative. The values contained therein were derived from CAP 385, Figure 29. It should be noted, that, unlike the NTOFP, fuel burn-off between altitudes must be taken into account, but the performance data may vary among aeroplane types.

When determining the mean weight for the height band traversed, the procedure may be found to be iterative. Also, where the descent gradient is appropriate to a mean weight and a mean altitude, the distance appropriate to the height change is plotted at the start and end of the height band. The number of points plotted — the number of height bands selected — should produce a smooth curve, as shown in Figure 6.26.

In Table 6.25 it is assumed that:

(i)   still air conditions prevail

(ii)   temperature = ISA + 15°C

(iii) fuel consumption during drift-down = 45 nm/ 1000 kg

(iv)   anti-icing is off.

The drift-down is from 30,000 ft to 2000 ft — the stabilising altitude — with two engines inoperative. The formula used in calculating the distance travelled during the descent is the same as given in 6.15:

$$\text{Horizontal distance (ft)} = \frac{\text{change in height (ft)} \times 100}{\text{Gradient (\%)}}$$

Conversion to nautical miles:

$$\text{Distance (nm)} = \frac{\text{change in height (ft)} \times 100}{\text{Gradient (\%)} \times 6080}$$

$$= \frac{16.44}{\text{Gradient (\%)}} \text{ per 1000-ft height change}$$

Table 6.25

Altitude x 1000 ft	Altitude Change x 1000 ft	Mean Altitude x 1000 ft	Start Weight kg x 1000	End Weight kg x 1000	Mean Weight kg x 1000	Descent Gradient %	Distance nm	Total Distance nm
30-26	4	28	167.5	167.1	167.3	−3.32	19.8	
26-22	4	24	167.1	166.6	166.8	−2.84	23.1	42.9
22-16	4	20	166.6	166.0	166.3	−2.41	27.3	70.2
18-14	4	16	166.0	165.3	165.7	−1.97	33.4	103.6
14-10	4	12	165.3	164.3	164.8	−1.45	45.3	148.9
10-6	4	8	164.3	162.7	163.5	−0.90	73.0	221.9
6-2	4	4	162.7	158.0	160.4	−0.31	212.1	434.0

Figure 6.26
Drift-down — 2 Engines Inoperative

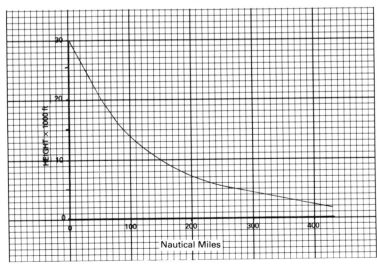

The effect of the wind component may be taken into account by factoring the horizontal distance travelled by GS/TAS, or by applying the factor of TAS/GS to the found gradient. (Note that the AN(G)R does **not** require the wind component to be factored, as in the take-off and landing cases).

6.21.2 Effect of Wind on Drift-down

The horizontal distances calculated from the foregoing formulae are for still air conditions; where there is an expected or forecast wind component, the effect on the drift-down flight path will, in the case of a headwind component, decrease the distance travelled thereby effectively increasing the net gradient; whilst in the case of a tailwind component the distance travelled will increase, effectively decreasing the net gradient. There are two methods by which wind component correction may be applied:

(i) By adjusting the net gradient:

Net gradient of climb	=	−2.50%
TAS	=	500 kt
Ground speed (G/S)	=	550 kt
Wind Component	=	50 kt (tail)

$$\text{Net gradient adjustment} = \frac{-2.5\% \times \text{TAS}}{\text{G/S}}$$

$$= \frac{-2.5\% \times 500}{550}$$

$$= -2.27\%$$

(The horizontal distance is now calculated using the corrected gradient of −2.27%.)

(ii) By adjusting the calculated horizontal distance:

$$\text{Corrected distance} = \frac{\text{calculated distance} \times \text{G/S}}{\text{TAS}}$$

6.22 Track Margins

Both requirements 7(4) and (5) permit the accountable track margins to be reduced to five nautical miles, where the operator is satisfied that the aeroplane's commander, taking into account the navigation aids available, will be able to maintain the intended track to the smaller tolerance. It is considered that an aeroplane equipped with Doppler or Inertial Navigation systems,

and a means of providing an error check, should be capable of tracking accuracies to those prescribed. Operators should assess the position fixing accuracy when assuming drift-down, CAP 360 requiring the information to be included in the Operations Manual, to cover drift-down where the route structure and aeroplane type make this desirable.

Landing Requirements

6.23   The landing phase of performance assessment concerns that portion of the flight starting 1500 ft above the aerodrome's landing surface, and ending when the aeroplane has come to a stop on the runway. The requirements are given in AN(G)R 7(6) and 7, and as with take-off, may be considered under two headings, each complementary: Airworthiness and Operational Requirements. Airworthiness is concerned mainly with structural limits and, to some extent, the scheduling of landing distances and climb gradients associated with the WAT limit. The operational limitations are concerned mainly with the variables to be considered in determining landing distance, landing climb, or WAT limit.

6.24   **Airworthiness requirements**
        The main aspect of these requirements is the Maximum Authorised Landing Weight (MALW), being a C of A limit, and also the absolute maximum landing weight (emergencies excepted) given in the Flight Manual. Other C of A requirements are involved when determining the landing distance required (means of retardation such as brakes, lift spoilers, and reverse thrust). On occasions, the MALW may be restricted to a lesser weight — the maximum permitted landing weight — by the application of operational requirements. It should also be understood that the maximum permitted, or maximum authorised landing weight could determine the maximum permitted take-off weight, depending on the sector distance to be flown and the fuel required.

        Compliance with airworthiness limitations is mandatory under the ANO.

6.25   Landing climb or WAT limit

AN(G)R 7(6) requires that:

the landing weight of the aeroplane will not exceed the maximum landing weight specified for the altitude and expected air temperature for the estimated time of landing at the aerodrome at which it is intended to land and at any alternate aerodrome (the WAT limit).

The landing WAT graph or curve ensures that, at a given weight, the aeroplane will have an acceptable minimum climb capability, with all engines operating and with one engine inoperative. The minimum climb gradients are derived from JAR 25.

6.25.1   Minimum Climb Gradients

The weight given by the landing WAT curve must not be:

(i)   greater than the weight given by the take-off WAT curve for the same pressure altitude and temperature, and

(ii) greater than the weight at which compliance with the following climb gradients is possible:

   (a)   Final en-route climb.
         With one engine inoperative, at 1500 ft above the aerodrome. The **net** gradient of climb shall be positive.

   (b)   Baulked landing climb.
         With all engines operating, at the aerodrome pressure altitude and in the landing configuration, the gross gradient of climb shall not be less than 3.2%.

   (c)   Discontinued approach climb.
         With the critical engine inoperative and the remaining operative engine(s) at take-off power, and at the aerodrome pressure altitude with the landing gear up, the gross gradient of climb shall not be less than:

         Twin-engined aeroplane: 2.1%
         Three-engined aeroplane: 2.4%
         Four-engined aeroplane: 2.7%

6.26   **Landing distance requirements**
AN(G)R 7(7) specifies the operational variables to be taken into account when determining the landing distance required which, basically, must not exceed the landing distance available at the destination or alternate aerodrome. When considering the operational variables, there are minor differences involved when using the forecast wind component, depending on whether or not the aeroplane is powered by turbo-jet engines, or turbo-propeller/piston engines. The differences are mainly concerned with the use of the forecast wind component in conjunction with 'alternate distance', when an alternate is designated in the flight plan. However, the operational variables common to both engine types are:

(i)   landing weight

(ii)   aerodrome pressure altitude

(iii)   the temperature in the International Standard Atmosphere (ISA) appropriate to aerodrome altitude

(iv)   a level surface, for a runway usable in both directions, and the average runway slope, for a runway usable in one direction only

(v)   still air conditions, in the case of the most suitable runway for landing in still air.

(vi)   the forecast wind component, for the most suitable runway required because of the forecast wind.

6.26.1 Turbo-jet-engined aeroplanes
If the aeroplane is powered by turbo-jet engines, then all aerodromes may be considered as destination aerodromes (the factor 0.95, as given in Figures 6.28 and 6.29, is not applicable). Using the forecast wind component becomes a straightforward operation when compared with turbo-propeller/piston engine-powered aeroplanes.

6.26.2 Turbo-propeller/piston-engined aeroplanes
In addition to the variables (i) to (iv), a proviso is made

in the Regulations relating to the type of aeroplane referring to the parameter to be used in the case of an alternate aerodrome designated in the flight plan; should this be the case, the landing distance required may be assessed as that applicable to an alternate aerodrome, when assessing the ability of the aeroplane to satisfy this requirement at the destination aerodrome. The implication of this proviso will be detailed more fully in the section 'determining limiting landing weights'.

Flight Manual landing data should incorporate the regulatory factored wind components, but a check should be made that it does.

6.27 Landing Field Length

An aeroplane's landing distance requirement may be determined by one of two sets of landing distance criteria: the Arbitrary Landing Distance, and the Reference Landing Distance, the main differences between them is shown in Table 6.30.

For both methods, the total landing distance required consists of two parts: an airborne distance, from the screen height over the threshold to touch down; and a ground roll, the result being factored by an appropriate factor, according to the method used. Illustrations of the main features of both methods are shown in Figures 6.28 and 6.29; in both figures, the alternate landing distance refers to turbo-propeller/piston-engined aeroplanes only.

6.27.1 Arbitrary Landing Distance
This is the gross horizontal distance required to land on a dry, hard surface from a screen height of fifty feet, and is determined in accordance with the conditions set out in Table 6.30.

6.27.2 Reference Landing Distance
This is the gross horizontal distance required to land on a reference wet, hard surface of defined friction characteristics, from a screen height of thirty feet, where the speed is the Maximum Threshold Speed (Vato + 15 kt) and touch down is at the reference touch-down speed, all determined in accordance with the conditions set out in Table 6.30.

Figure 6.28
Arbitrary Landing Distance Required

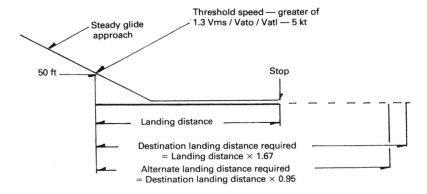

Figure 6.29
Reference Landing Distance Required

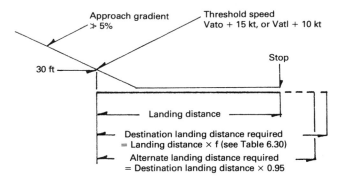

6.28   **Limiting Landing Weight (turbo-jets)**
As with take-off (where distances available and required were matched to obtain a field length limited take-off weight), for landing, the distances required and available are matched to provide a field length limited landing weight.

Referring to 6.26, it should be apparent that, in order to obtain a maximum landing weight for one runway, two calculations are required: one for still air, and one for forecast wind component. Thus, for a multi-runway aerodrome two calculations per runway will be required, with the most limiting landing weight (having considered the AN(G)R) taken to be the maximum landing weight for that aerodrome. The Regulation can be interpreted, in terms of landing weight, as: the field length limited landing weight shall be the **lower** of

(i)   the highest weight obtainable in still air

(ii)   the highest weight obtainable, using the forecast wind component

Both may refer to different runways.

Therefore, when considering an aerodrome with one runway, the limiting landing weight for both field

Table 6.30

	Arbitrary	Reference
Screen Height	50 ft	30 ft
Approach	Steady glide approach with CAS not less than 1.3 Vs to 50 ft	Not greater than 5% gradient.

Threshold speed	Greater of Vato and Vat1 minus 5 kt	Vat max =
		     Vato + 15 kt, or
		     Vat1 + 10 kt

Temperature	ISA	ISA
Runway surface	Dry, hard, paved	Reference wet, hard, paved surface of defined friction characteristics
Braking	Brakes only; other means may be used conditionally	Wheel brakes plus other means, provided they are practical and controllable
One engine inoperative	Required if 'other means' of braking are engine-dependent	Accountable
Field length factor (destination)	1.82 (covering operational variables — excessive height and speed at the threshold, prolonged float and a reduced surface friction)	Greater of 1.24-0.1Cdg/Cda, or 1.11 (f). One engine inoperative. Greater of 1.19-0.1Cdg/Cda, or 1.08 (f), scheduled landing distance is the greater of the two above
Field length factor (alternate)	Destination landing distance x 0.95	Destination landing distance x 0.95

Note: Cgd/Cda is the ratio of effective ground-borne and airborne aerodynamic drag coefficients, and is the total drag of the aeroplane at sixty-five per cent of the reference touch-down speed, with the wheel brakes inoperative, when the aeroplane is landed using the technique adopted for determining the reference landing distance. For wet runways, the field length factor becomes 1.92 for turbo-jets **not** fitted with effective reverse thrust. The alternate field length factor applies to turbo-propeller/piston-engined aeroplanes only.

length and aerodrome becomes that for still air, unless the runway is used in one direction only, with a tailwind component.

Considering an aerodrome with more than one runway, and remembering to compare 'like with like', the limiting weight for the aerodrome becomes the **lower** of:

(i) the highest weight of the two runways, using still air conditions

(ii) the highest weight of the two runways, using the forecast wind component

When determining the maximum landing weight at the flight planning stage, it should be remembered, that, in addition to considering the wind component, the other variables to be used include: aerodrome pressure altitude; ISA temperature at that altitude; runway slope; and, of course, the landing distance available. The parameters to be used when determining maximum landing weight are given in Table 6.31.

Table 6.31

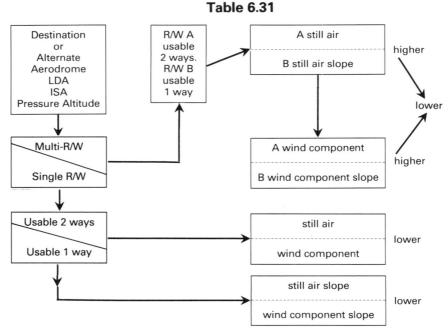

6.28.1 Turbo-propeller/piston-engined aeroplanes
The foregoing information relating to turbo-jet aero-

planes also applies to propeller-driven aeroplanes. However, as indicated in 6.26, an added dimension is introduced in the form of a 'designated alternate'. Where this is invoked, in conjunction with considering the forecast wind component, the less stringent landing distance appropriate to an alternate aerodrome (destination landing distance × 0.95) may be applied at the destination.

Thus, for propeller-driven aeroplanes the interpretations of the AN(G)R given in 6.28, whilst also being valid here, are supplemented when an alternate aerodrome is designated in the flight plan and used, in the forecast wind component case, by the performance assessor being able to use the destination landing distance available on the alternate landing distance scale of the landing chart in use. This effectively means that an extra five per cent of destination landing distance may be used which, in turn, will lead to an enhanced landing weight. It should be pointed out, that when considering a forecast wind velocity at right angles to the direction of the landing runway, a wind component of zero will result, but will still allow the assessor to invoke the rule of the 'designated alternate'; whereas, still air conditions will not allow the same privilege. Table 6.32 shows the parameters to be used when determining the maximum landing weight, using all rules, including those pertaining to the 'designated alternate'. In the table:

Alt. dist. = destination landing distance available used on the alternate landing distance scale

S/A = still air

W/C = wind component

Dest. dist. = destination landing distance

6.29 Landing — Contaminated runways

The risks and factors involved when operating on a contaminated runway are covered in 6.7 and, although dealing with effects on take-off performance, the recommendations contained therein are also applicable to landing, in particular: **the operation should be avoided wherever possible.**

However, should such operations be unavoidable.

the pilot should be aware of the risks involved, the procedures to be used, the operating techniques to be adopted and the performance corrections to be applied. When landing the main problems arising are:

(i)   braking capability on a surface having a low coefficient of friction

(ii) hydroplaning

(iii) directional control during the ground roll

(iv) wheel spin-up on touchdown

Table 6.32

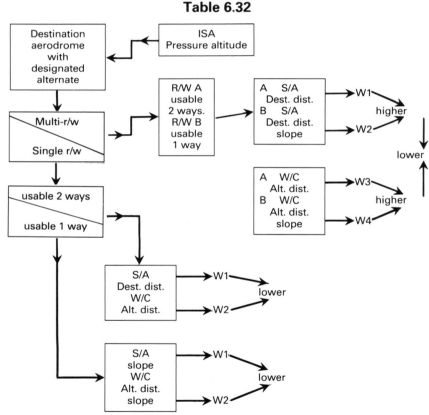

6.29.1   Landing distance required
As pointed out in 6.7.4, the difficulty in measuring or predicting the actual coefficient of friction associated with contaminated runways was the reason why scheduled performance data, in this case, can only be

regarded as the 'best data available' or, as shown in some Flight Manuals, 'advisory' data.

The landing distance required for landing in contaminated conditions is determined initially as that for a normal, wet-dry surface, and is then corrected to that appropriate to a landing surface with a braking coefficient of friction of 0.05, which is typical of an ice-covered runway, or one on which hydroplaning may occur. In determining this distance, it is assumed that all engines are operating and that all means of retardation are used; in addition to this required data, information should also be provided giving the effects on low friction landing distance when:

(i) using less than full reverse thrust (up to 50%)

(ii) passing through the screen height in excess of the target speed (up to 10 kt)

Low friction landing distances may be estimated but, where approval is given for operations on runways covered by more than 3 mm of precipitation, precipitation drag should not be included in the estimate. It is necessary that data must be provided giving the distance required for landing in conditions where low braking coefficients of friction exist, the data given in CAP 385 p31 being considered representative of such information, but it is advisory only.

6.29.2 Re-assessment of landing performance

Performance assessment at the departure stage is concerned with the despatch of the aeroplane only and, whilst it is unlikely that an aeroplane would be despatched to a destination involving a contaminated runway, it is possible that the aeroplane could arrive at the destination/alternate after or during contamination. In this event, and depending on the prevailing conditions and operational necessities, a hold prior to landing (if possible) could well suffice to alleviate the risks involved, or a diversion to a safe alternate may prove more beneficial. It is during these 'decision' stages that a re-assessment of landing performance may be made. However, it does not require contaminated conditions to re-assess landing performance, it may be carried out at any time, or under any conditions, prior to landing. When re-assessing, the **actual** conditions should be used in all cases:

(i)   the advisory effects of temperature (using actual temperature)

(ii) the actual wind component

(iii) the slope of the landing runway, if any

(iv) the actual landing weight.

SECTION THREE

7. Aeroplanes Classified in Performance Group C

7.1   The requirements of AN(G)R 8, in conjunction with the associated airworthiness requirements of BCAR, Section K, form the basis for providing an adequate, broad and uniform level of safety for aeroplanes not exceeding 5700 kg; so that, in the event of engine failure after take-off and the initial climb, a forced landing should not be necessary. Although accountability for engine failure on take-off is not a requirement, the desired level of safety is achieved by the airworthiness requirements and conditions.

Regulation 8 provides the basis on which performance assessment is to be conducted by determining the aeroplane performance available during the various phases of flight, under assumed failure conditions with appropriate and stipulated meteorological conditions. This enables the flight to be planned and the take-off weight adjusted in such a way as to provide the minimum acceptable performance levels. Since the requirements are to be satisfied prior to flight, some assumptions have to be made and, in the interest of standardisation, the Regulations stipulate the various parameters and conditions to ensure compliance with each part of the Regulations.

BCAR, Section K comprises the minimum airworthiness requirements and constitutes the basis for the issue of a C of A, required by the ANO. These requirements were originally written for small aeroplanes, simple in design and construction, and not exceeding 2730 kg. As a result of further study of potential light aeroplane development, the scope of the section was widened to allow for certification of similar types of aeroplanes not exceeding 5700 kg.

Group C aeroplanes are usually multi-engined and

have a positive en-route performance with one engine inoperative. Additional operating regulations are included for landing distance requirements for aeroplanes with short field landing capabilities, the data for which is included in their Flight Manuals.

The data needed to satisfy Group C requirements is similar to that for Group A aeroplanes.

7.2 Take-off Requirements

These basically come under three main headings: Maximum Authorised Take-off Weight; WAT or Climb Limits; and Take-off Distance Requirements.

7.2.1 Maximum Authorised Take-off Weight

This is both a structural and an airworthiness limitation, not within the bounds of the AN(G)R and given in the Flight Manual, and **must not be exceeded**.

7.2.2 Maximum Take-off Weight — Altitude and Temperature

The Regulation requires, that:

at the start of the take-off run, the aeroplane weight does not exceed the maximum take-off weight specified for the altitude and air temperature at the aerodrome at which the take-off is to be made (the WAT limit, or sometimes referred to as the second segment climb limit).

The WAT graph, or curve, displayed in the Flight Manual ensures that the aeroplane has an acceptable climb or acceleration capability with all engines operating, and with one engine inoperative. The WAT requirements are contained in Section K (K2-4) with the aeroplane having to comply with the minimum climb performance under the following conditions:

(i) Take-off climb.
At the altitude of the take-off surface, the gross climb performance in free air shall not be less than five per cent, or a rate of climb of 400 fpm, whichever is the greater, in the following configuration:

airspeed: V2
flaps: take-off setting
landing gear: retracted*
engines: all engines not exceeding maximum take-off power

(ii) Second-segment climb

For aeroplanes with a stalling speed in excess of 60 kt when in the landing configuration and at maximum weight, the gross gradient of climb, in free air, at the altitude of the take-off surface, shall not be less than zero in the following configuration:

airspeed: V2
flaps: take-off setting
landing gear: retracted*
engines: critical engine inoperative and propeller feathered; operating engine(s) not exceeding maximum take-off power

* Landing gear is assumed to be extended, unless it is possible (irrespective of a failure of the critical engine, at all speeds between 1.2Vso and V2), to extend and retract the landing gear, each in not more than seven seconds. If the landing gear is power operated, at least two complete cycles of operation are possible after failure of the critical engine. The purpose of the seven-second time period is concerned with the reduction of drag.

(iii) Final take-off climb.

One engine inoperative; at a gross height of 1500 ft, the gradient of climb shall not be less than 0.8% in the following configuration:

airspeed weight: corresponding to those which would exist on reaching 1500 ft gross height when establishing the data from which the NTOFP, with one engine inoperative, is derived
flaps: en-route setting

landing gear: retracted

engines: critical engine inoperative, propeller feathered, and operating engine(s) not exceeding maximum continuous power

In addition to the above, the WAT limited take-off weight may be limited further by the 'all engines operating' baulked landing requirements of a gross gradient of climb of 3.2%, at the altitude of the landing surface. The take-off WAT curve gives the highest aeroplane weight at which the given gradients can be met, and plots the weight against aerodrome pressure altitude and ambient temperature. The foregoing data is summarised in Table 7.1 and a diagram of the various segments is given in Figure 7.2

Table 7.1

Gross gradient of climb
Nil ground effect

Segment	Configuration	%	Rate of climb 80	Rate of climb 100	Rate of climb 120	Remarks
	G/S knots	%	80	100	120	
1	one eng. inop.	nil	nil	nil	nil	
2	one eng. inop.	nil	nil	nil	nil	
2	all eng. op.	5.0	400	510	608	
3	one eng. inop.	nil	nil	nil	nil	level segment
4	one eng. inop.	0.8	65	80	97	

Figure 7.2
WAT — CLIMB

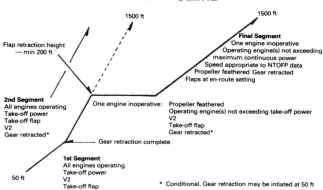

7.2.3   Take-off Distances
AN(G)R 8(2) requires, that for the given operational variables of:

(i)   the weight of the aeroplane at the start of the take-off run

(ii)   the aerodrome pressure altitude

(iii)   the aerodrome ambient temperature

(iv)   the average slope of the surface of the aerodrome in the direction of take-off over the EDA

(v)   not more than 50% of the reported headwind component, or not less than 150% of the reported tailwind component

(A)   the take-off run required must not exceed the take-off run available, and

(B)   the **take-off distance required** must not exceed the **Emergency Distance Available.**

7.2.3.1   Distances scheduled in the Flight Manual
BCAR, K2–3 describes the manner in which, for certification purposes, the take-off field lengths are factored for inclusion as performance data in the aeroplane's Flight Manual:

(a)   Take-off run required.
The take-off run required shall be 1.15 times the gross horizontal distance to accelerate on a dry hard surface, from the starting point, and to attain a speed equal to V2 when the aeroplane is held on, or near to the ground.

N.B. It is not intended that the technique used for determining the TOR required should form part of the scheduled take-off technique.

(b)   Take-off Distance Required.
The take-off distance required shall be 1.25 times the gross distance from the starting point to the screen height of fifty feet, derived when the aeroplane is operated from a dry,

73

hard surface, when the aeroplane is accelerated on, or near to the ground; a transition to climbing flight is then effected, and a speed of not less than V2 is attained at the screen height. In complying with these requirements, the following control requirements must be satisfied:

(i) in the event of a sudden failure of the critical engine at any point in the take-off, conducted using the recommended technique, at any speed up to V2, it shall be possible to prevent lateral divergence from the intended flight path of more than thirty feet

(ii) where the aeroplane is airborne at a speed below V2, it shall be possible, in the event of failure of the critical engine, to re-land. In showing compliance with this requirement, appropriate allowance shall be made for delays in recognition of engine failure and taking the necessary action.

It may be noted at this point that the field length requirements include no specific acccountability for engine failure during take-off, hence, no V1/VR and consequently no decision speed V1. The inclusion of a twenty-five per cent margin on the TOD required to fifty feet (the 1.25 factor) and the requirement that this distance must not exceed EDA, ensures a fair probability of success in any attempt to abandon the take-off at speeds approaching VR. Diagrams of the scheduled distances are shown in Figures 7.3 and 7.4. As discussed in 4.2, aerodrome declared distances are listed in the Air Pilot as TORA, TODA and EDA, but for some aerodromes likely to be used by Group C aeroplanes, the information available may not be quite so comprehensive, sometimes only the overall runway dimensions are given. Unless more specific data is available, the EDA should be taken as the given runway length.

Figure 7.3

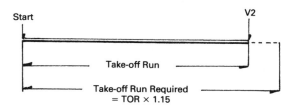

Figure 7.4

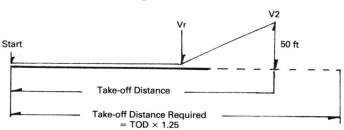

7.2.4 Field Length Limited Take-off Weight

As stated in 7.2.3, under the conditions of the operational variables given therein, the TORR and TODR must not exceed the TORA and EDA, respectively (this is illustrated in Figure 7.5).

In practice, it is more usual to determine the field length limited take-off weight, given the operational variables in 7.2.3 (ii) to (v) inclusive, and the aerodrome declared distances.

To find the required weight it is usual to match the TODR to the available runway length, so that the take-off run need not be considered. If advantage is to be taken of any available stopway to obtain a higher weight, TORR must be matched with TORA, and TODR with EDA; also, it is necessary to check that the stopway is available as clearway, which will be the case only if EDA is equal to, or less than TODA.

To ensure that the field length limited weight is determined accurately, commensurate with safety, it is recommended that the weights appropriate to all three distances are calculated, remembering that since TODR must not exceed EDA, the weight calculation appropriate to the EDA is carried out on the take-off distance chart, or graph, if no specific EDA chart is available. The maximum field length limited weight is the most limiting of the three calculated weights and the WAT limit, assuming that obstacle clearance, en-route and landing conditions are all not critical. Although V1/VR is not considered, some Group C aeroplanes' Flights Manuals may include advisory data in respect of distance requirements for rejected take-offs.

Figure 7.5

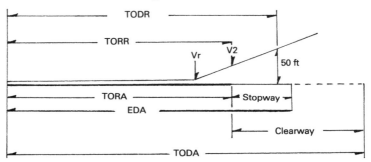

7.3 Flight Manual Data

It is advisable to check that Flight Manual scheduled data incorporates the field length factors given in 7.2.3.1 (a) and (b), and the factored wind component as required by the AN(G)R. (In many Flight Manuals, the factored wind component is **not** incorporated, despite BCAR requirements.)

Temperature data is usually displayed in terms of ISA deviation, appropriate to aerodrome pressure altitude, with a direct ambient temperature reference. Slope limitations are the same as for Group A aeroplanes — 2% up/down — but some manuals may only cover slope up to 1.5%, in which case it is permitted to extrapolate to the maximum 2%, but the Flight Manual should be checked for extrapolation details.

7.4 Runway Conditions

Unlike Group A aeroplanes, the operational variables applicable to Group C aeroplanes do not include accountability for runway surface conditions, the requirements being predicated on a 'dry hard surface'.

However, the data is also applicable to wet runways. where operations are planned from unpaved surfaces. The advice of the CAA Safety Regulation Group should be sought, if the Flight Manual does not contain corrections for the type of runway surface. The performance effects of wet and dry grass are difficult to predict, the subject not lending itself to definitive treatment with the effect on rolling friction of almost infinitely variable combinations of climatic conditions and soil types.

Where the Flight Manual contains no data, in addition to the CAA advice the following should be borne in mind when assessing the effects:

Grass runways

	Length
Fresh cut:	2–3 in
Short:	3–4 in
Typical summer aerodrome:	4–6 in
Long:	6–10 in

Rolling friction coefficients appropriate to the length and condition of the grass have been calculated, giving the following increments to the factored take-off distance for a typical small aeroplane:

Short dry grass:	8%
Short wet/long dry grass:	12%
Long wet grass:	22%

The soil condition is given as follows:

Hard — when taxying the aeroplane makes no wheel marks.

Firm — when there are wheel impressions but no rutting.

Soft — when there is marked wheel rutting.

It is recommended that given the latter, the operation should be suspended.

Where specific corrections and/or advice is given in the Flight Manual, it should be considered as the minimum acceptable data. Operations from strips or aerodromes contaminated with snow, slush, ice, or extensive standing water are **not** recommended, the contents of 6.7.2 being equally applicable here.

Obstacle Clearance

7.5 The requirements to be satisfied in respects of the NTOFP and obstacle clearance are contained in AN(G)R 8(3) and (4), while BCAR, Section K (K2-3) covers the airworthiness aspects. In the case of Group C aeroplanes, both 'all engines operating' and 'one engine inoperative' flight paths may be expected to be considered. In each case, obstacles are required to be cleared by a vertical distance of thirty-five feet. Provision is made for turning, but if the change of direction exceeds fifteen degrees, vertical clearance is increased to fifty feet; the turn must not be planned to have a radius of less than that specified in the Flight Manual. If turn data is not included in the Flight Manual, the radius of a steady, fifteen-degree banked turn may be calculated using the following formula:

$$\text{radius of turn (ft)} = 1/3 \, TAS^2, \text{ where TAS is in knots.}$$

In addition to this, the CAA Safety Regulations Group should be consulted for information and advice relating to the particular type of aeroplane. In both NTOFP cases, net climb performance data should be used

7.6 **The Take-off Flight Path Area — the Funnel**
Since two flight paths may be considered, it follows that two flight path funnels should be calculated so that obstacles may be identified. Definitions of the areas to be considered are given in the AN(G)R and can be summarised as:

Configuraton	Semi-width at origin	Divergence	Maximum semi-width	Origin
All engines operating	75 m	Nil	75 m	end of TODR
One engine inoperative	75m	Distance/8	900 m	end of EDA

Plan, and elevation illustrations of the above areas are shown in figures 7.6 and 7.7, respectively

Figure 7.6
All engines operative

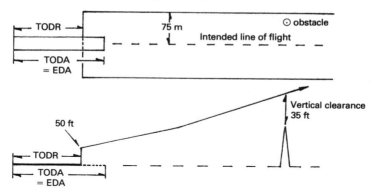

Figure 7.7
One engine inoperative

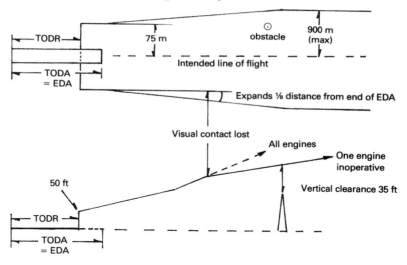

7.7   The Net Flight Path

The minimum net performance data to be complied with when considering the net flight path is given in BCAR, K2-3 as follows:

(i)   All engines operating.
       The net flight path shall be the gross flight path diminished by a climb gradient of two per cent, or, where the aeroplane is accelerating in level

flight, the acceleration element shall be obtained from an acceleration equal to the gross acceleration diminished by an acceleration equivalent to a two per cent gradient of climb.

(ii) One engine inoperative.
With the critical engine inoperative, the net flight path is as (i) above, except that 0.8% is subsitituted for two per cent.

The one engine inoperative flight path is the path which, in the event of take-off in adverse/restricted visibility conditions, has to be assumed to apply from the point at which it becomes necessary to fly by reference to instruments. In satisfying (i) and (ii) above, the following conditions are prescribed:

Gross performance shall be fifty feet to flap retraction height in the take-off configuration at V2, except that landing gear retraction may be initiated at fifty feet. From flap retraction height to 1500 ft, at a speed not less than V2 appropriate to the flap setting. At and above V2, the speed shall be based on the climb performance at constant speed and the acceleration performance at a constant height. The engine power used must not exceed maximum take-off power up to the time limit for use of that power; thereafter not exceeding maximum continuous. The minimum height at which the flaps may be retracted to the en-route setting shall not be less than 200 ft.

Operational variables to be taken into account when calculating the NTOFP are similar to those for Group A aeroplanes (given in 6.13).

As indicated in AN(G)R 8(4) and above, for Group C aeroplanes the 'see and avoid' principle is invoked for obstacle clearance. If the pilot can see the obstacle, it is assumed that avoiding action can be taken in the event of engine failure or other emergency, in which case, only the 'all engines operating' flight path needs to be considered. This is plotted from the point above the end of TODR — fifty feet above reference zero, to 1500 ft above the aerodrome. Any obstacles within seventy-five metres of the intended line of flight, as shown in Figure 7.6, must be cleared by the required thirty-five feet (or fifty feet in a turn).

Where the take-off is to be made in conditions where the cloud base obscures the obstacle from the pilot's view for any period of time before reaching 1500 ft, the 'one engine inoperative' net flight path must be assumed to apply, from the point on the 'all engines operating' flight path at which it becomes necessary to fly by instruments (height of the cloud base). In this case, an obstacle in the expanding funnel — as shown in Figure 7.7 — must be cleared by the required margin.

For Group C aeroplanes, an engine is assumed to have failed immediately the aeroplane enters cloud with a significant obstacle to be cleared. This may well present operators with problems relating to weather minima because the limiting take-off weight from some runways may be a function of the assumed (or reported) height of the cloud base. Whilst the aim of the requirement is to determine a safe take-off weight, compatible with obstacle clearance, the following points should be noted:

(a) If an engine failure occurs during the initial climb after take-off, the flight should be discontinued and a safe procedure for landing at the departure aerodrome, or a nearby aerodrome, should be available for the pilot to follow

(b) Turns in the NTOFP are permitted, to avoid obstacles, remembering the height clearance provisions associated with turns and obstacle clearance.

Figure 7.8
All engines operating

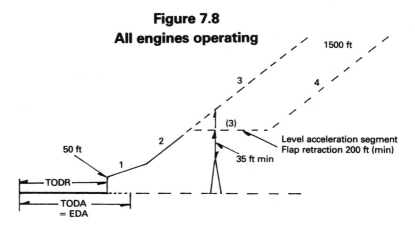

81

At severely obstacle-limited aerodromes, the NTOFP with one engine inoperative should always be examined in the light of (a) and (b) above.

Profiles of the flight paths thus far discussed are shown in Figures 7.8 and 7.9.

Figure 7.9
One engine inoperative

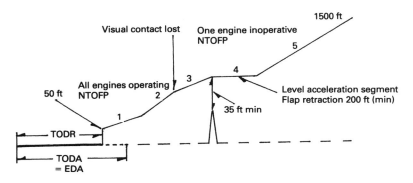

7.8 Calculating the NTOFP and Obstacle Limited Take-off Weight

Determining the obstacle limited take-off weight is usually done by calculating and constructing the NTOFP, using the net climb performance data contained in the Flight Manual. The true height-versus-distance relationship of each segment is calculated and plotted, and the obstacle clearance height (obstacle height + thirty-five feet) is then compared with the constructed flight path. If necessary, a second NTOFP at a decreased or increased weight is constructed and again compared. The obstacle limited take-off weight is then determined by linear interpolation between the two flight paths. The choice of the initial weight is usually taken to be the field length limited take-off weight, with the second weight at an appropriate difference.

The following example, embracing all the procedures thus far discussed, has been determined using the performance data contained in the current Specimen Performance Charts for aeroplanes certified in Performance Group C: (CAP 551 1st Edition).

Details

Aerodrome pressure altitude:	sea level
OAT:	+20°C
TORA:	2165 ft
EDA:	2895 ft
TODA:	2990 ft
Slope:	Nil
Wind:	Nil
Surface:	Dry, hard

The aeroplane is fitted with de-icing equipment

Flap retraction height:	400 ft
Height of cloud base:	300 ft
Obstacle	
Distance from the end of TODA:	2610 ft
Height above end of TODA:	300 ft
Distance from intended line of flight:	170 m

Calculations

Fig 9   WAT   12,500 lb +

Fig 10 TORA $\dfrac{2165 \times 100}{103} = 2102 = 12,500$ lb

Fig 11 EDA $\dfrac{2895 \times 100}{103} = 2810 = 12,000$ lb

Fig 11 TODA $\dfrac{2990 \times 100}{103} = 2902 = 12,150$ lb

Field length limited weight = 12,000 lb (EDA)

Note: the factor 100/103 is to allow for de-icing equipment fitted — notes.

Funnel:

2990 − 2895 = 95 + 2610 = 2705/8 = 338 ft

338 ft = 103 m

semi-width = 103 + 75 = 178 m

Therefore, obstacle is accountable at 5600 ft from the start of TORA.

Flight Path:

Weight = 12,000 lb   TODR = 2810 × 1.03 (de-icing)

Horizontal distance (HD) = 2895 ft

                                              Total HD

Seg 1 Fig 13 HD = 786 ft   3681 ft

          Fig 14 Ht = 126 − 4   = 122 ft

Seg 2 Ht change $300 - 122 = 178$ ft
    Fig 15   Grad $= 10.1\% - 0.5\%$
                                    (de-icing)
                                      $= 9.6\%$

$$HD = \frac{178 \times 100}{9.6} = 1854 \text{ ft} \qquad\qquad 5535 \text{ ft}$$

Seg 3 Ht change $400 - 300 = 100$ ft
    Fig 16   Grad $= 5.55\% - 0.5\%$
                                      $= 5.05\%$

$$HD = \frac{100 \times 100}{5.05} = 1950 \text{ ft} \qquad\qquad 7515 \text{ ft}$$

Seg 4 Fig 17 $HD = 1300 \text{ ft} + 2\%$
                                  $= 1326 \text{ ft} \qquad\qquad 8841 \text{ ft}$

Seg 5 Ht change $1500 - 400 = 1100$ ft
    Fig 18   Grad $= 6.65\% - 0.5\%$
                                        $= 6.15\%$

$$HD = \frac{1100 \times 100}{6.15} = 17{,}886 \text{ ft} \qquad\qquad 26{,}727 \text{ ft}$$

When plotting the calculated flight path it will be found that, at the planned weight of 12,000 lb, the flight path profile at the obstacle location gives a height of approximately 302 ft — the required obstacle clearance height being 335 ft. This is shown in Figure 7.10, which also shows the 'all engines operating' flight paths for the weights involved in this example, for comparison. It would appear that weight must be reduced in order to attain the required height; the second weight chosen for the net flight path would depend, to some extent, on the amount by which the first flight path infringed the obstacle clearance requirements, bearing in mind a figure for ease of calculation. Thus, in this case, a second weight of 11,000 lb has been selected. This second flight path is calculated in the same way as the first, using the same format.

Figure 7.10 shows, that at the lesser weight, the flight path clears the obstacle by approximately fifty-seven feet. Remembering the obstacle clearance height is 335 ft, linear interpolation, by graph or arithmetic, will give the optimum take-off weight of 11,400 lb.

Figure 7.10
Flight Paths

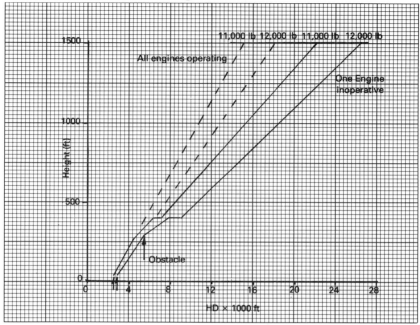

Figure 7.11

Segments 1–3

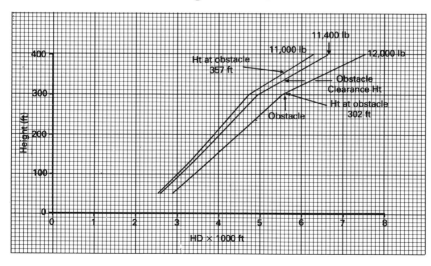

Figure 7.10 illustrates the two required flight paths, consisting of five segments — the second segment comprises the 'all engines operating' and 'one engine inoperative' cases of reaching flap retraction height — and showing that the first flight path infringes the obstacle clearance requirements by approximately thirty-three feet, with the second flight path well clear of the obstacle at 357 ft. Figure 7.11 shows segments one to three of the two flight paths — on a magnified basis — confirming the heights found previously. Figure 7.12 goes on to show the graphical and arithmetical deter-mination of the obstacle limited weight by interpolation, and it is quite clear that, in this case, the obstacle limited take-off weight is 11,400 lb.

Figure 7.12
Obstacle Limited Take-off Weight

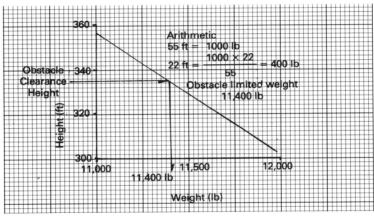

7.9 Turns

The take-off flight path funnel used for obstacle identi-fication purposes involving a turn, or turns before reaching 1500 ft is illustrated in plan view for the 'all engines operating case' in Figure 7.13, whilst the 'one engine inoperative' funnel is shown in Figure 7.14. Both are similar in respect of dimensions, to the straight climb-out flight path.

Because of changing aeroplane configuration and speed in the first and fourth segments, turns can be accurately accounted for only in the second, third and fifth segments. The 'all engines operating' data may include a performance margin allowing for changes in heading (second segment) but the 'one engine inoperative' data (third and fifth segments) may usually include a smaller margin allowing for a total change of heading not exceeding fifteen degrees. The minimum radius of turn to be assumed in the appropriate segment is determined for a steady rate-one turn (three degrees per second) followed by assessment of the total heading change required. These two parameters combine to give:

(a)   the horizontal distance travelled during the turn

(b)   the height lost due to the turn.

The horizontal distance travelled in the turn is used to locate the point from which the segment continues, whilst in order to determine the distance to achieve a given height, the segment under consideration is required to 'regain' the height lost due to the turn.

Flight Manual data should be checked before use for information on allowances incorporated for turns.

Figure 7.13

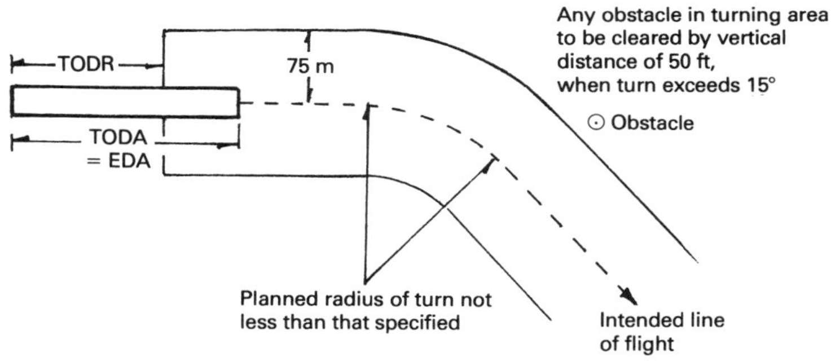

Figure 7.14

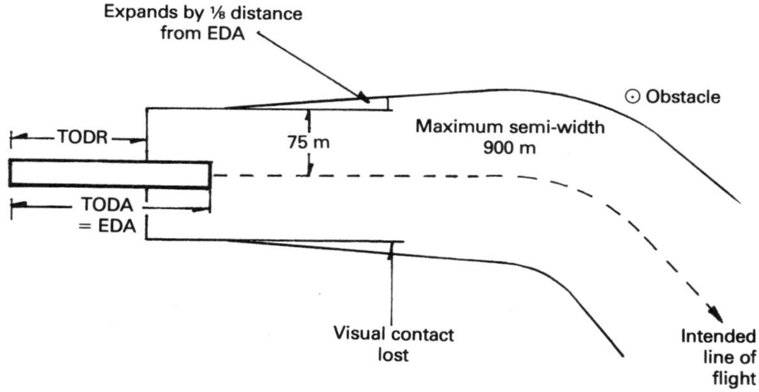

7.10 Effect of Wind on the NTOFP

Climb gradient data contained in the Flight Manual will usually include a wind correction grid, thus allowing the extraction of wind corrected gradients. However, the data should be checked that it incorporates the factored wind components in accordance with the AN(G)R. Examination of a climb gradient chart with a wind correction grid will show that:

(a) a headwind component will effectively increase the gradient of climb, so decreasing the horizontal distance travelled over the segment under consideration

(b) a tailwind component will have the opposite effect of (a)

Should a Flight Manual not include wind corrected climb data, wind corrected distance may be calculated using either of the following formulae:

(i) by adjustment of the gradient of climb

$$\text{wind corrected gradient} = \frac{\text{given gradient} \times \text{TAS}}{\text{G/S}}$$

or

(ii) $$\text{corrected distance} = \frac{\text{calculated distance} \times \text{G/S}}{\text{TAS}}$$

(where G/S = TAS $^+/_-$ factored wind component)

The effect of wind on a flight path involving a turn is to displace the aeroplane's track downwind by a distance equal to: wind speed (feet/sec) × time to turn (secs), calculated at a rate-one turn through the required heading change.

7.11 Effect of Slope on Obstacle Clearance

Similar to the case of Performance Group A aeroplanes, the slope of the take-off surface is not included in the operational variables to be taken into account when determining the NTOFP and obstacle clearance. However, also similar to Group A aeroplanes, the slope of the take-off surface will affect the NTOFP in relation to obstacle height, in the same manner as described in 6.14 (i) and (ii), and illustrated in Figure 6.23.

Generally, a down-sloping take-off surface will afford a higher take-off weight, both in field length and obstacle limitation; whilst an up-sloping take-off surface will have the opposite effect. Referring to the worked example in 7.8, but in this case using slope values of one per cent up and down, a comparison may be made, as shown in Table 7.15.

Table 7.15

Maximum take-off weights
Take-off surface slope

	1% down	zero	1% up
Field limited (EDA)	12,400 lb	12,150 lb	11,650 lb
Obstacle limited	11,560 lb	11,400 lb	11,190 lb

As can be seen in Table 7.15, a downward slope of one per cent would increase the field length limited weight by approximtely 2.05%, and the obstacle limited weight by approximately 1.4%; whereas, a one per cent upward slope would decrease the weights by approximately 4.11% and 1.84%, respectively. At this point, it should be emphasised that any benefit arising (in terms of enhanced take-off weight) from a down-sloping surface **should not be taken into account**. It would be advisable to treat any such enhancement as a safety margin. However, in the case of an upward slope, calculating the obstacle limited take-off weight should be done with some care.

7.12 Flight Manual Data

Climb data contained in the Flight Manual should usually include allowance for fuel used during the take-off and climb through the various segments, thus allowing entry to the charts using the take-off weight, and also the aerodrome pressure altitude and ambient temperature, where these are variable inputs. Where actual flap retraction height differs from that on which the Flight Manual data was derived, the Manual should contain instructions relating to the adjustments to be made for the differing heights. In all cases the performance assessor should always check Flight Manual data before use.

7.13 Summary

Obstacle clearance is predicated on the 'see and avoid' principle and, where that principle cannot be invoked because of restricted visibility, it must be assumed that the aeroplane has suffered an engine failure at the point where visual contact with the obstacle is lost. In view of this, two funnels may be considered: one for 'all engines operating', and one for 'one engine inoperative'; the former of constant width originating at the end of TODR, and the latter also starting at the end of TODR but expanding at the rate of one-eighth distance from the end of EDA, to a maximum semi-width of 900 m. Where the obstacle can be seen, only the 'all engines operating' flight path needs to be considered.

In the event of a low cloud base ruling out the possibility of visual clearance, the 'one engine inoperative' flight path must apply from the point where visual contact is lost. In both cases the flight path ends at 1500 ft above the aerodrome.

Obstacle limited weight is determined by the interpolation of two flight paths, calaculated and constructed for differing weights. Any weight benefit arising from a down-sloping take-off surface **should not be taken into account**.

En-route Requirements

7.14   The en-route requirements for Group C aeroplanes contained in AN(G)R 8(5), comprise basically the following:

In the expected meteorological conditions (including temperature), in the event of an engine failure after reaching 1500 ft above the departure aerodrome, the aeroplane must be able to continue the flight to a suitable aerodrome for landing, maintaining at least the minimum safe altitude for the route, as prescribed in the Company Operations Manual, appropriate to the aeroplane type. On arrival over the suitable aerodrome, the aeroplane must be capable of maintaining 1500 ft above that aerodrome. In assessing the ability of the aeroplane to perform accordingly, it is assumed that the operative engine(s) is/are operated at maximum continuous power, and, prior to engine failure, the flight altitude did not exceed the performance ceiling appropriate to the estimated aeroplane weight at the engine failure point.

7.15   **Gradients**
The ability of the aeroplane to comply with the requirements must be assessed using the data appropriate to the En-route Net Gradient of Climb with one engine inoperative and the 'all engines operating' Performance Ceiling, as given in the Flight Manual.

7.15.1 All Engines Operating Performance Ceiling
This is the altitude at which, for the given weight, the pressure rate of climb is not less than 150 fpm. The airspeed used in establishing this data should not be less than that used in showing compliance with the final take-off climb requirement — 7.2.2. (iii) — and the speed selected for establishing the 'one engine inoperative' data. The speeds may vary with aeroplane weight but not with altitude and temperature.

7.15.2 One Engine Inoperative Data
The net gradient of climb with the critical engine inoperative will be the gross gradient of climb diminished by a gradient of one per cent.

7.16   **Drift-down**
Although not forming part of the AN(G)R requirements, a drift-down procedure may be assumed, the maximum permissible altitude at which it is assumed to start being the lower of (i) the 'all engines operating' performance ceiling, (ii) the planned or actual flight altitude. Drift-down is calculated in the same manner as for Group A aeroplanes, outlined in 6.12.1 and Figure 6.26; the main differences between the groups being the weights involved and the starting altitudes, otherwise all else, including wind effect, is the same. Note that for Group C aeroplanes, no account may be taken for the jettisoning of fuel.

7.17   **Flight Manual Data**
En-route data contained in the Flight Manual will usually consist at least of an 'all engines operating' Performance Ceiling Chart, predicated on the criteria given in 7.15.2. In addition to the latter, the en-route climb speeds should also be found, both for 'all engines operating' and 'one engine inoperative'. The Performance Ceiling Chart will provide, for a given weight and temperature — illustrated sometimes in

terms of ISA deviation — the performance ceiling which does not prohibit flight at a higher altitude but, as net data, represents the ceiling which the aeroplane may be relied on to achieve on a regular basis.

Net gradients are used for calculating the horizontal distance travelled, as in 6.12.1; the effect of fuel burn during the altitude changes is not taken into account in the charts, it being necessary to enter the chart with the estimated, or actual weight appropriate to the mean altitude of the height change. However, compared with Group A aeroplanes, the fuel used in descent is rather insignificant and sometimes a mean weight may be used throughout.

Landing Requirements

7.18   Landing requirements for Group C aeroplanes are contained in AN(G)R 8(6), (7) and (8) which cover the operational variables to be taken into account for both normal and short field landing operations, the latter being covered in (8) with the main differences between it and the normal field length operation being the screen heights used:

(i)   with all engines operating, any height between thirty and fifty feet in the UK, and fifty feet elsewhere

(ii)   with one engine inoperative, fifty feet in the UK and elsewhere.

Provisions attached to the short field landing operation consist of an available, suitable, alternate aerodrome being designated in the flight plan, under conditions of 'one engine inoperative' and insufficient landing distance available at the destination; and the short field landing technique being prohibited, if it is intended to land at night, or when the cloud ceiling or ground visibility forecasts for the estimated time of landing at the destination or alternate aerodrome are less than 500 ft and one nautical mile, respectively.

7.19   **Airworthiness Requirements**
Complementary airworthiness requirements are contained in BCAR, Section K and cover such aspects as

WAT climb gradients, structural limitations, and conditions to be complied with in determining both the normal and the short field landing lengths (these conditions will be discussed in turn when considering the landing field lengths). **Airworthiness structural limitations are mandatory**.

7.20 **WAT — Landing**

Regulation 8(6) states: *the landing weight will not exceed the maximum landing weight specified for the altitude and expected air temperature for the estimated time of landing* (the WAT limit).

The landing WAT graph or curve ensures that, at a given weight, the aeroplane will have an acceptable minimum climb capability, with all engines operating and with one engine inoperative. The given weight must not be:

(i) greater than the weight given by the take-off WAT curve for the same pressure altitude and temperature

(ii) greater than the weight at which compliance with the following climb gradients is possible:

(a) Final en-route climb — with one engine inoperative at 1500 ft above the aerodrome, the gross gradient of climb shall not be less than 0.8% (net gradient is positive).

(b) Baulked landing climb — with all engines operating at the aerodrome pressure altitude and in the landing configuration, the gross gradient of climb shall not be less than 3.2%.

7.21 **Landing Distance**

The Regulation stipulates that the landing distance required, specified as being appropriate to destination and alternate aerodromes, from a height of fifty feet, does not exceed seventy per cent (factor = 1.43) of the landing distance available on the most suitable runway for a landing in still air, and on the runway that may be required for landing because of forecast wind. The operational variables to be taken into account are:

(i) the landing weight

(ii) the aerodrome pressure altitude

(iii) ISA temperature appropriate to the pressure altitude of the aerodrome

(iv) a level surface, in the case of runways usable in both directions; and the average slope of the runway, in the case of runways usable in one direction only

(v) still air conditions, in the case of the most suitable runway for landing in still air conditions

(vi) not more than fifty per cent of the forecast headwind component, or not less than 150% of the forecast tailwind component, in the case of a runway required for landing because of the forecast wind.

7.21.1 Normal (conventional) Field Length

In addition to the operational variables to be taken into account, the normal field length requirement is predicated on the measured landing distance on a dry, hard surface, from a screen height of fifty feet and factored according to the number of engines operative. Thus, the landing distance required shall be the greater of:

Figure 7.16

Landing Distance Required — Destination and Alternate Aerodromes

Normal field length operations

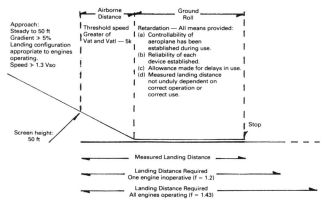

(i) the landing distance required with all engines operating × 1.43

(ii) the landing distance required with one engine inoperative × 1.20

The conditions associated with the conventional field length, and the composition of the measured landing distance are shown in Figure 7.16.

Figure 7.17

Landing Distance Required — Destination and Alternate Aerodromes

Short Field length operations

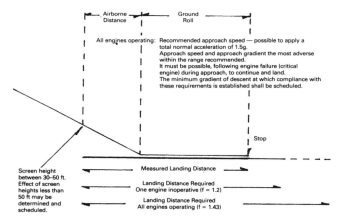

7.21.2 Short Field Length

The requirements of the short field technique are that the landing distance required (with all engines operating and with one engine inoperative, to land in accordance with specified short field data) does not exceed the landing distance available on the most suitable runway for a landing in still air, and on a runway required because of the forecast wind, at the destination or alternate aerodrome. The height from which the distance is measured is given in 7.18 with the provisos therein.

An aeroplane will usually achieve a short landing capability by the use of reverse thrust and an approach which is steeper and slower than that of the conventional technique. The requirements permit approaches to screen heights lower than fifty feet (with a lower limit of thirty feet), within certain constraints imposed by handling conditions, but a consequence of using low approach speeds and reverse thrust to obtain short landing distances with all engines operating is the possibility of a relatively large increase in the distance, following an approach with one engine inoperative. BCAR and the operational rules in effect recognize this and, as a result, the landing distance required is the greater of:

(i)   the measured landing distance × 1.43, when measured from a height between thirty and fifty feet with all engines operating

(ii)   the measured landing distance from fifty feet × 1.20, with one engine inoperative.

However, note that the short field landing technique is **not** permitted with one engine inoperative.

In both normal and short field landings, the ground roll provisions, which deal mainly with retardation devices, are the same. A comparison of Figures 7.16 and 7.17 will show the differences between the techniques.

7.22 Public Transport Safety Factor

The 'gross landing distance required shall not exceed seventy per cent of the landing distance available' requirement, is sometimes referred to as 'The Public Transport Safety Factor', and should be applied at all times when the Flight Manual states that it is not included in its scheduled data. As 100/70 equals 1.43, this factor may also be used.

7.23 Limiting Landing Weight

As in the case of Group A aeroplanes, the field length limited landing weight is found by matching the landing distance available with the landing distance required, using the operational variables given in 7.21 (ii) to (vi). In the case of Group C aeroplanes, the alternate field factor is 1.0, thus there is no alternate landing distance provided — all aerodromes, in terms of landing distance available, being treated as destinations.

The field length limited landing weight appropriate to destination and alternate aerodromes (assuming one runway) is the **lower** of the highest weight given in still air conditions, and the highest weight given in forecast wind conditions.

For multi-runway aerodromes, each runway should be treated separately and a comparison made of the maximum weights obtained, as follows:

(i)   calculate the highest weight obtainable for each runway using still air conditions. Select the highest weight.

(ii)   calculate the highest weight obtainable for each runway using the forecast wind component. Select the highest weight.

(iii) the maximum field length limited weight is the **lower** of the weights selected at (i) and (ii).

The maximum permitted landing weight for the aerodrome now becomes the **lower** (more restricting) of:

(a)   the maximum authorised landing weight

(b)   the WAT limited landing weight

(c)   the field length limited weight.

Table 7.18 illustrates a simple algorithmic process in order to assist in identifying the parameters to be used when determining the field length limited landing weight.

7.24   **Grass runways**

If the landing is to be carried out on a grass runway, an adjustment to the scheduled 'hard, dry, paved' data will be necessary; typically, the factor to be applied in the case of dry grass would be in the order 1.1, whilst that for wet grass would be 1.3. Again, the Flight Manual should contain information on the appropriate increment to be applied. Should the Flight Manual contain unfactored data for grass landings, then it should be remembered that the effect of grass landing factor(s) is compounded with the required field length factor (if not incorporated) of 1.43. For example, for a landing on dry grass with unfactored field length data, the factors to be applied would be 1.43 × 1.1, whilst for a landing on wet grass the factors would be 1.43 × 1.33. General Aviation Safety Leaflet No.7 — Performance, is recommended to the reader.

Table 7.18

7.25 Re-assessment of Landing Weight

The information contained in 6.29.2 is equally applicable to Group C aeroplanes, with of course the Group C reservations.

Landings on contaminated runways should be avoided whenever possible. However, in the event of such operations being, or becoming, unavoidable, pilots should be aware of the risks involved, the procedures to be followed, the techniques to be adopted and the performance corrections to apply.

SECTION FOUR

8. Aeroplanes Classified in Performance Group D

8.1   AN(G)R 9 gives the operational requirements applicable to aeroplanes certified in Performance Group D; whilst the complementary airworthiness requirements are contained in BCAR, Section K, applying to aeroplanes not exceeding 5700 kg MTWA.

These requirements cover aeroplanes with no specific provision for performance after engine failure, thus it may be assumed that Group D aeroplanes are essentially single-, or multi-engined but not necessarily capable of maintaining height with one engine inoperative. The Regulations therefore comprise operational rules designed to ensure suitable operating weights when this class of aeroplane is used for public transport purposes.

The introductory paragraph of the AN(G)R contains the first operational rule applicable to this group:

a Performance Group D aeroplane shall not fly for the purpose of public transport at night or when the cloud ceiling or visibility at the aerodrome of departure, and forecast for the estimated time of landing at the destination or any alternate aerodrome, are less than 1000 feet and one nautical mile, respectively.

8.2   Take-off Requirements

8.2.1   Maximum Authorised Take-off Weight
This is a structural limitation not covered by the AN(G)R but given in the Flight Manual as an airworthiness limitation, and **must not be exceeded**.

8.2.2   Maximum Take-off Weight — Altitude and Temperature
As with the previous groups described, the AN(G)R requires, that at the start of the take-off run the

aeroplane's weight does not exceed the maximum take-off weight specified for the altitude and temperature at the aerodrome at which the take-off is to be made — the WAT limit.

Unlike the previous groups, the WAT graph or curve for Group D aeroplanes ensures the aeroplane has an acceptable climb capability, with all engines operating only. The climb capability specified in K2-4 ensures that the aeroplane complies with the following minimum climb performance under the associated conditions:

(i) Take-off climb:
At the altitude of the take-off surface, the gross gradient of climb in free air shall not be less than five per cent, or a rate of climb of 400 fpm, whichever is the greater in the following conditions:

Airspeed: V_2
Flaps: Take-off setting
Landing gear: Retracted*
Engines: Not exceeding maximum take-off power

* Landing gear is assumed to be extended unless it is possible, at speeds between $1.2V_{so}$ and V_2, to extend the gear in not more than seven seconds, and retract in no more than seven seconds, for twin-engined aeroplanes with power operated landing gear, at least one complete cycle of operation, at the prescribed operating rate, if possible, after failure of the critical engine. The purpose of the seven-second period is concerned with the reduction of drag.

(ii) Final take-off climb:
All engines operating, at a gross height of 1000 ft the gross gradient of climb shall not be less than two per cent or a rate of climb of 200 fpm, whichever is the greater, in the following conditions:

Airspeed: Not less than $1.2 V_{sl}$
Flaps: En-route setting
Landing gear: Retracted
Engines: Not exceeding maximum continuous power

Weight: Corresponding to that which would exist on reaching a gross height of 1000 ft in establishing the data from which the NTOFP is derived.

In addition to the above, the WAT limited take-off weight may be further limited by the 'all engines operating' baulked landing requirement of a gross gradient of climb of 3.2% at the altitude of the landing surface.

The foregoing data is summarised in Table 8.1. A

Table 8.1

Gross gradient of climb
Nil ground effect

			Rate of climb		
			Ground Speed Knots		
			60	80	100
Segment	Configuration	%			
1	all engines operating	Nil	Nil	Nil	Nil
2	all engines operating	5.0	300	400	510
Final	all engines operating	2.0**	120	160	200

** Or 200 rpm rate of climb, whichever is the greater.

Figure 8.2

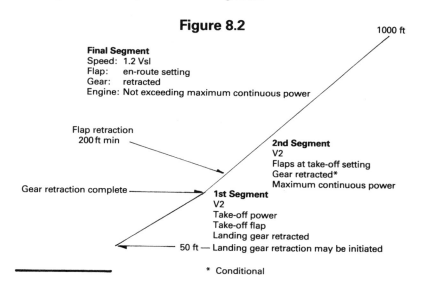

1000 ft

Final Segment
Speed: 1.2 Vsl
Flap: en-route setting
Gear: retracted
Engine: Not exceeding maximum continuous power

Flap retraction
200 ft min

Gear retraction complete

2nd Segment
V2
Flaps at take-off setting
Gear retracted*
Maximum continuous power

1st Segment
V2
Take-off power
Take-off flap
Landing gear retracted
50 ft — Landing gear retraction may be initiated

* Conditional

diagram of the WAT climb and appropriate configuration is shown in Figure 8.2

8.2.3 Take-off Distance Requirements
The take-off distance requirements of Group D aeroplanes are identical to those applicable to Group C aeroplanes, the only difference being the weights involved. The reader is therefore referred to 7.2.3 and 7.2.4 in conjunction with a comparison of Regulations 8(2) and 9(2).

Obstacle Clearance

8.3 The NTOFP for Performance Group D aeroplanes is calculated and plotted from a screen height of fifty feet, at the end of the take-off distance required to a height of 1000 ft above the departure aerodrome level, with all engines operating only. The intended flight path must clear all obstacles by a vertical distance of thirty-five feet, assuming the obstacle(s) to be within seventy-five metres of the intended line of flight.

The aeroplane may make a turn to avoid obstacles but, as in the previous groups, the radius of turn may not be less than that specified in the Flight Manual, and if the turn exceeds a fifteen-degree change of direction, the vertical clearance requirement is increased to fifty feet in the turn. The statement made in 7.5 referring to lack of turn information in the Flight Manual also applies to this group.

8.4 **The Take-off Flight Path Area — Funnel**
The area in which, for purposes of obstacle clearance, obstacles may be identified is defined in AN(G)R 9(3) (b) and is summarised in Table 8.3.

Table 8.3

Configuration	Semi-width at origin	Divergence	Max. semi width
All engines operating	75 m	Nil	75 m

Plan and elevation illustrations of the intended flight path, the funnel, and a flight path involving a turn are shown in Figures 8.4, 8.5 and 8.6, respectively.

8.5 **The Net Flight Path**
The NTOFP, based on the minimum net performance data and associated conditions contained in BCAR K2-3, shall be the gross take-off flight path with all engines operating, diminished by a gradient of climb of two per cent. The gross performance to comply with the foregoing is with the aeroplane in the take-off configuration (except that the landing gear may be retracted at fifty feet), at V2 appropriate to the flap setting, up to a gross height of 200 ft, below which no change in flap configuration is permitted. The climb is based on the use of take-off power for the full period of time permitted for use of that power.

The operational variables to be taken into account when computing a flight path involving obstacles are the same as for Groups A and C aeroplanes. Unlike Group C, there is no 'see and avoid' principle, nor do the parameters take into account the height of the cloud base and the associated reference to instrument flight and the inference of engine failure.

Figure 8.4

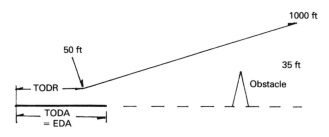

Figure 8.5

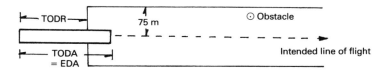

Figure 8.6

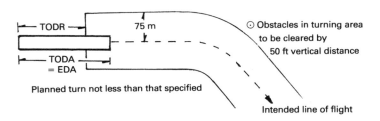

8.6 **Calculating the NTOFP and Obstacle Limited Take-off Weight**

The calculation of the NTOFP in respect of obstacle limited take-off weight assumes a similar process to that carried out for Group C aeroplanes, but with minor differences:

(i) only the 'all engines operating' data is used

(ii) only two segments are considered

(iii) the omission of a specified flap retraction height (minimum 200 ft)

(iv) nil reference to cloud base and the associated implications of engine failure.

To illustrate how the obstacle limited take-off weight and the NTOFP are determined, the following example is given (the data used is that appropriate to the CAA publication — Specimen Performance Charts for aeroplanes certified in Performance Group D — current at the time of writing, which is considered to be representative of the group's publication of performance data). The example embraces the normal procedures thus far covered:

Details:

Aerodrome pressure altitude:	1000 ft
OAT:	+20°C
TORA:	1900 ft
EDA:	2340 ft
TODA:	2400 ft
Slope:	nil
Wind:	nil

Aeroplane is fitted with de-icing equipment
Obstacle: 2000 ft from the end of TODA;
             260 ft above the end of TODA;
             55 m from intended line of flight.

Calculations:

Fig 9 WAT: 6000 lb
Fig 10 TORA: 1900/1.03 = 1846 ft = 6000 lb
Fig 11 EDA: 2340/1.03 = 2271 ft = 5900 lb
Fig 11 TODA: 2400/1.03 = 2330 ft = 6000 lb
Field length limited take-off weight = 5900 lb (EDA)
The obstacle at 55 m from intended line of flight is
significant.

Flight Path 1:   Total
                                                        HD
Weight = 5900 lb   TODR = 2270 × 1.03 =   2340 ft
Seg 1: Fig 13   HD   = 753 ft   3093 ft
       Fig 14   Ht   = 103 − 3   = 100 ft
Seg 2: Fig 15   Gradient = 8.9% − 0.5 = 8.4%
                     Ht change = 1000 − 100 = 900 ft

$$\text{HD} = \frac{900 \times 100}{8.4}$$

                     = 10,714 ft   13,807 ft

Ht at obstacle = 208 ft — too low.

Flight Path 2:   Total
                                                        HD
Weight = 5000 lb   TODR = 1800 × 1.03 =   1854 ft
Seg 1: Fig 13   HD   = 708 ft   2562 ft
       Fig 14   Ht   = 126.5 − 3.5 = 123 ft
Seg 2: Fig 15   Gradient = 12.65% − 0.5= 12.15%
                     Ht change = 1000 − 123 = 877 ft

$$\text{HD} = \frac{877 \times 100}{12.15}$$

                     = 7218 ft   9780 ft

Ht at obstacle = 347 ft
Difference in ht (5900 and 5000 lb) = 139 ft
Required height: 295 ft (260 + 35)

$$52 \text{ ft} = \frac{900 \times 52}{139} = 335 \text{ lb}$$

Obstacle limited take-off weight = 5335 lb.

Figure 8.7 illustrates the calculated flight paths, the inset graph showing the linear interpolation used to determine the optimum take-off weight to clear the obstacle.

Figure 8.7
Net Take-off Flight Path and Obstacle Clearance

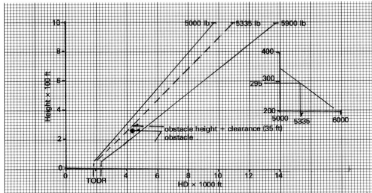

8.7   Turns
The net data used to determine the flight path will usually include a performance margin for relatively minor changes of direction during the climb. However, where it is necessary to change direction significantly before reaching 1000 ft, the amount of turn must be considered. For Group D aeroplanes turns may only be considered (for planning purposes) in the second segment, the Flight Manual data giving the radius of turn, depending on the aerodrome pressure altitude, temperature, and take-off weight. The resultant radius obtained is that for a steady rate-one turn (three degrees per second), and is used to determine the horizontal distance travelled using the following formula:

$$HD = \frac{\text{Radius of turn}}{57.3} \times \text{heading change}$$

where radius of turn is given in feet and heading change in degrees and HD = horizontal distance.

The HD travelled is then used to locate the point from which the segment is continued. Flight Manual data may or may not contain data relating to height loss during the turn; should the data be included then it should be used as for Group C aeroplanes, but Flight Manual data should be checked before use for information on allowances included for turns.

8.8 **Wind effect on the NTOFP**
This is identical to that described for Performance Group C aeroplanes (detailed in 7.10).

8.9 **Effect of runway slope on obstacle clearance**
Also identical to that for Group C aeroplanes outlined in 7.11, except that the operating weights are considerably reduced. An example of the problem in 8.6 has been completed, using a slope over the take-off distance of one per cent up/down, with the result that a comparison may be made of take-off weights as outlined in Table 8.8.

Table 8.8

	Maximum take-off weights (lbs) Take-off distance slope		
	1% down	**Nil**	**1% up**
Field limited (EDA)	6100*	5900	5740
Obstacle limited	5440**	5335	5200

* MTWA: 6000 lb.   ** Based on TOW: 6000 lb.

A one per cent downward slope will increase the maximum take-off weights for both field length and obstacle limited cases by approximately 3.4% and 1.95%, respectively; whereas a one per cent upward slope will decrease the respective weights by 2.7% and 2.5%. Also, as in the case of Group C aeroplanes, **it would be prudent to disregard any increase in take-off weight afforded by a downward slope**. With an upward slope, calculations should be treated with some care.

8.10 **Flight Manual data**
Net flight path data relating to flight path calculations and obstacle clearance incorporates the fuel used during the take-off and climb, thus allowing entry to the charts using the take-off weight; similar allowances are made in the case of aerodrome pressure altitude and temperature, but reported wind components will probably require factoring in accordance with the AN(G)R. Once again, the performance assessor should check before use.

8.11 **Summary**
Obstacle clearance for Group D aeroplanes is, compared to the other groups, relatively straightforward in that (a) the take-off flight path funnel is basically rectangular in shape with no divergence, the semi-width (seventy-five metres) being constant throughout, even in a turn; (b) only the 'all engines operating' net flight path is considered, consisting of two segments up to 1000 ft above the departure aerodrome. Obstacle clearance weight is determined by graphical or linear interpolation, after constructing two flight paths (as shown in Figure 8.7). Turns may only be considered in the second segment. Any weight benefit accruing from a downward sloping take-off distance should be ignored and treated as a safety margin.

En-route Requirements

8.12 The en-route requirements contained in AN(G)R 9(4) basically require that the aeroplane must, in the expected meteorological conditions (including temperature), in the event of engine failure, after reaching a height of 1000 ft above the departure aerodrome, be able to continue the flight to a suitable aerodrome for landing, maintaining at least the minimum safe altitude, as prescribed in the Company Operations Manual, appropriate to the aeroplane type; arriving over the suitable aerodrome at 1000 ft from which a safe landing may be made. In assessing the ability of the aeroplane to perform accordingly, it is assumed that the operative engine(s) is/are operated at maximum continuous power and, prior to engine failure, the flight altitude did not exceed the performance ceiling appropriate to the estimated weight at the engine failure point. Obviously, the foregoing refers to multi-engined, Group D aeroplanes only.

8.13 **Gradients**
The ability of the aeroplane to comply with the requirements must be assessed using the data appropriate to the En-route Net Gradient of Climb with one engine inoperative, and the 'all engines operating' performance ceiling, as given in the Flight Manual.

8.13.1　All engines operating performance ceiling
This is the altitude at which the pressure rate of climb is not less than 150 fpm; the airspeed used in establishing the data shall not be less than that used to comply with the final take-off climb requirement — 8.2.2 (ii) — and the speed selected for the 'one engine inoperative' data. The speeds may be varied with weight, but not with altitude and temperature.

8.13.2　One engine inoperative data
The net gradient of climb with the critical engine inoperative is the gross gradient of climb, diminished by a gradient of one per cent.

8.13　**Drift-down**
The information for and calculation of drift down is identical to that for Group C aeroplanes, covered in 7.16, the main differences being the weights and starting altitudes involved. Wind effect is identical; also, fuel jettison may not be credited.

8.15　Flight Manual data
Data contained in the Flight Manual will usually comprise the 'all engines operating' Performance Ceiling (8.13.1), and the 'one engine inoperative' Net Gradient of Climb (8.13.2). The performance ceiling in the Flight Manual does not prohibit flight at a higher altitude but, as net data, it represents the ceiling which the aeroplane may be regularly relied on to achieve.

The gradient obtained from the Net Gradient data may be used to calculate the horizontal distance travelled during the descent (as in 6.21.1). Effect of fuel burn-off during the descent is not allowed for in the data, it being necessary to enter the chart with the actual or estimated weight, appropriate to the altitude (mean) used in the calculation. 'All engines operating' and 'one engine inoperative' climb speeds are also contained in the Flight Manual.

Landing Requirements

8.16　The landing requirements covered in AN(G)R 9(5) and (6) give the basic operational rules in respect of WAT limitation and the operational variables to be taken into account when determining the normal field length requirement with all engines operating only. There are no short field length requirements for Group D aeroplanes.

8.17 Airworthiness requirements

The complementary airworthiness requirements are contained in BCAR, Section K, covering the WAT climb gradients to be met, structural limitations, and the conditions to be complied with (see 8.19 and Figure 8.9) in determining the data given in the Flight Manual. Airworthiness structural limitations, as given in the Flight Manual, are **mandatory**.

8.18 WAT limitation — Landing

Regulation 9(5) outlines the WAT limitation as:

the landing weight of the aeroplane will not exceed the maximum landing weight specified for the altitude and expected air temperature for the estimated time of landing at the destination, and at any alternate aerodrome

From the airworthiness aspect, complementing the above, the landing WAT graph or curve ensures the aeroplane has an acceptable minimum climb capability, with all engines operating, at the given weight which must not be:

(i)   greater than the weight given by the take-off WAT graph for the same pressure altitude and temperature

(ii) greater than the weight at which compliance with the baulked landing climb gradient can be met, i.e. with all engines operating, at the aerodrome pressure altitude and in the landing configuration, the gross gradient of climb shall not be less than 3.2% (255 fpm rate of climb, at 80 kt ground speed).

The baulked landing requirement given above will be combined with the take-off climb requirements to form a single WAT graph, giving both maximum take-off and landing weights.

8.19 **Landing Distance required**
The operational variables to be taken into accunt when determining the landing distance required are identical to those for Groups A and C, given for the latter in 7.21. In respect of airworthiness requirements, the landing distance required will be the Measured Landing Distance with all engines operating, multiplied by 1.43 (100/70); the measured landing distance is the gross horizontal distance required to land on a dry, hard surface, from the screen height, and come to a complete stop. The conditions associated with the landing distance requirements are depicted in Figure 8.9, including the composition of measured landing distance.

8.20 **Similarities**
Several aspects of the landing distance requirements applicable to Group D aeroplanes are identical to those for Group C, thus, the following references to Section 7 of this guide should be read as also applying to this section:
8.21 Flight Manual data (ref 7.22).
8.22 Limiting landing weight (ref 7.23).
8.23 Grass runways (ref 7.24).
8.24 Re-assessment of landing weight (ref 7.25).

In addition, Table 7.18 also applies to this section when calculating the maximum landing weight.

Figure 8.9
Landing Distance Required — Destination and Alternate Aerodromes

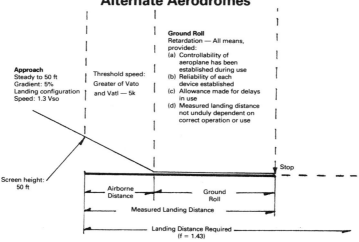

111

SECTION FIVE

9. Aeroplanes Classified in Performance Group E

9.1   The requirements contained in AN(G)R 10, applicable to Performance Group E aeroplanes, complement the airworthiness requirements of BCAR, Section K to provide a performance level that may be broadly equated to Group C twin-engined, and Group D single-engined aeroplanes. This group is limited to aeroplanes of a MTWA of 2730 kg, the requirements permitting the use of simplified methods of performance scheduling are contained in a document other than a Flight Manual (e.g. Owner's Manual, Pilot's Operating Handbook, Manufacturers' Instructions or similar documents any of which may be accepted as an alternative to the Approved Flight Manual).

The data contained in the 'simplified' document has not been subjected to the same control and scrutiny as the scheduled data contained in Flight Manuals. Thus, the operational constraints on Group E aeroplanes are generally more severe than those of other groups. The C of A should specify the performance information used and any additional limiting performance conditions applicable to the aeroplane type, and thus should always be examined in this context. Performance data may be presented in graphical or tabular form.

Regulation 10 contains the rules by which, at the proposed take-off weight and under assumed engine failure and stipulated meteorological conditions, the requisite safety levels throughout the various phases of flight are achieved; as in the other groups, the Regulation outlines the various parameters and conditions to be used when ensuring compliance with each part of the Regulation.

9.2 Operational limitation

Although placed at the end of AN(G)R 10, the first operational limitation — 10(2) — should be considered at the outset of performance assessment — a Performance Group E aeroplane shall not fly for the purpose of public transport at night, or when the cloud ceiling and visibility prevailing at the departure aerodrome and forecast for the estimated time of landing at the destination or alternate aerodrome, are less than 1000 ft and one nautical mile, respectively. However, the foregoing limitation is not applicable if the aeroplane is capable, in the en-route configuration and with one engine inoperative, of a rate of climb of 150 fpm.

9.3 Take-off requirements

The take-off requirements applicable to Group E aeroplanes differ somewhat from those of other performance groups, the main differences being the presentation of performance requirements and data; the performance levels to be achieved are directly related to specific rates of climb without benefit of a WAT graph or curve. In turn, the required rates of climb are dependent on:

(i) flight conditions, i.e. whether or not the flight is to be conducted by reference to instruments, in which case, the 'one engine inoperative' configuration is assumed

(ii) type of landing gear — fixed or retractable

(iii) one engine being inoperative.

Presentation of the performance data is usually by means of simple tables of distances and rates of climb appropriate to pressure altitude and temperature and a given aeroplane weight; distances are usually gross measured distances (i.e. unfactored), whilst the rates of climb are pressure rates.

9.3.1 Take-off climb limits

A Group E aeroplane shall not fly for public transport purposes unless the weight at the start of the take-off run, at the pressure altitude and temperature at the departure aerodrome, enables the following requirements to be met:

(i)   In the en-route configuration with all engines operating, within the specified maximum continuous power conditions, the aeroplane is capable of a rate of climb of 700 fpm, if it has retractable landing gear, or 500 fpm if it has fixed landing gear

(ii)   In the en-route configuration, if it is necessary for the aeroplane to be flown solely by reference to instruments for any period of time before reaching the minimum safe altitude appropriate to the first stage of the route to be flown, as specified in the aeroplane's Operations Manual, with one engine inoperative, the aeroplane is capable of a rate of climb of 150 fpm.

Thus the climb limited weight will be the more restricting of that which allows a rate of climb of 700/500 fpm, and that allowing a rate of climb of 150 fpm. The calculations involved in determining the climb limited weight may be usually straightforward, arithmetical proportion, whereby the difference between the rate of climb available at a given weight and the rate of climb required — (i) or (ii) above — is equated to a weight difference to be used as a weight correction factor.

9.3.2 Take-off distance
The only field length requirement to be considered is the gross 'all engines operating' distance to a screen height of fifty feet. The AN(G)R requires that this distance, when factored by 1.33, must not exceed the EDA. When determining the distance required, the following must be taken into consideration:

(i)   take-off weight

(ii)   aerodrome pressure altitude

(iii)   aerodrome air temperature

(iv)   not more than fifty per cent of the reported headwind component, or not less than 150% of the reported tailwind component, for take-off.

The field lengths given in the performance data will usually be the measured take-off distance to fifty feet, this being the measured distance to accelerate on a dry, hard surface with all engines operating from the start of the take-off run, to effect a transition to climbing flight, and to attain a screen height of fifty feet, at a speed not less than V2. Figure 9.1 illustrates the composition of the TODR.

It should be noted that there is no take-off run requirement for Group E aeroplanes, it being usual to equate the factored TODR to the runway length, to ensure that lift-off occurs before the end of the runway. Also, should the declared EDA contain stopway, the stopway should be checked for use as clearway, otherwise the factored TODR should be equated to the available runway length.

Figure 9.1

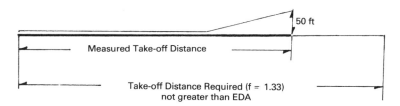

9.4 **Field length limited take-off weight**
As with the other performance groups, to obtain the field length limited take-off weight, the distances available are matched with distances required, allowing for the operational variables in 9.3.2 (ii–iv) inclusive, not forgetting that the distance available in this case must be divided by the regulatory 1.33. The following example illustrates the methods used in calculating the field length and climb limited weights, and uses the performance data contained in CAP 508:

Example:
Aerodrome pressure altitude: 5000 ft
OAT: +22°C
TORA: 1500 m
EDA: 1530 m
TODA: 1530 m
Slope: nil
Air: still
Runway surface: hard, dry and paved

Calculations:

ISA temperature at 5000 ft $= +5°C$
ISA deviation $= +17°C$

Climb limits: (i) 700 fpm, all engines operating
(ii) 150 fpm, one engine inoperative

CAP 508 (i) not limiting
(ii) 5000 ft PA and ISA $+17°C$
ROC available at MTOW (2450 kg)= 93 fpm
ROC required $= 150$ fpm
Difference $= 57$ fpm
Wt reduction = 100 kg/60 fpm

$$57 \text{ fpm} = \frac{100 \times 57}{60} = 95 \text{ kg}$$

Climb limited weight = 2450−95 = 2355 kg
Field limits:
EDA = 1530 m Factored = 1530/1.33 = 1150 m
TODR at MTOW (2450 kg) = 1197.5 m

$$\% \text{ decrease in weight} = \frac{1150 \times 100}{1197.5} = 96.03 = 3.97\%$$

5% = 100 kg, 3.97% = 79.4 kg

Field limited take-off weight=2450−79.4=2370.6 kg

Thus the maximum permitted take-off weight for the aerodrome is 2355 kg (climb limited).

The foregoing problem does not include wind effect which is accounted for in a similar way to that shown above.

9.5 Take-off — grass runways

The field length data given in the performance document will have been measured on a dry, hard, paved runway. Operations on grass runways will require the measured data to be incremented, or factored, the amount being dependent on the state and length of the grass, the factor(s) for which should be contained in the performance document. However, it should be appreciated that the advisory factors/increments to be applied to the measured data are the minimum acceptable for the given condition. Should the grass runway information not be included in the performance document, or when the validity of data is in doubt, advice should be sought from the Safety Regulation Group of the CAA.

Table 9.2 gives a guide to the various factors to be applied for given conditions, and should be used as a 'cross check' on any of the advised factors given in the performance document, which should be used in preference to any other type of table of increments.

It should also be appreciated that the given factors are cumulative, i.e. they should be applied in addition to the regulatory factors (e.g. for a take-off on short, wet grass, the distance required to fifty feet would be equal to the measured distance multiplied by 1.25 × 1.33, thus making a total factor of 1.6625). All factors given, for whatever condition, should be used in a similar manner. Additional advice given concerning grass runways is given in 7.4.

It should also be remembered, at this point, that operations from contaminated runways, by any class of aeroplane, should be avoided whenever possible.

Table 9.2

Condition of grass	Increase in distance to 50 ft	Factor
Dry — short 5"	20%	1.2
Long — between 5-10"	25%	1.25
Wet — short	25%	1.25
long	30%	1.30

N.B. The effect on ground roll will be greater.

9.6 Runway Slope

It may be noted that AN(G)R 10(1) (b) does not include runway slope among the variables to be taken into account when calculating the TODR, or the field length limited take-off weight. However, since runway slope can have a significant effect on an aeroplane's take-off performance, it would be prudent to make some adjustment, especially in the case of an uphill slope. The effect of an uphill slope is to reduce the aeroplane's acceleration throughout the ground roll, thus entailing an increase in the TODR.

To obtain the increase in distance required, it is first necessary to determine the mean acceleration on a level runway using the formulae:

$V^2 = 2as$, where $V = V2$ speed (ft/sec);
$a =$ acceleration (ft/sec^2); $s =$ TODR to fifty feet.

Thus (using the data contained in CAP 508), at sea level, in ISA conditions at MTOW (2450 kg), the aeroplane would require 685 m to attain a height of fifty feet at a speed of 95 kt (under ISA conditions, IAS = TAS).

$$95 \text{ kt} = 160.44 \text{ ft/sec}$$
$$685 \text{ m} = 2246.8 \text{ ft}$$

$$a = \frac{V^2}{2s} = \frac{160.44^2}{2 \times 2246.8} = 5.728 \text{ ft/sec}^2$$

Reduction in acceleration due to slope $=$ Lg, where L $=$ gradient of slope and $g = 32.2$ ft/sec^2.
Thus:

$$1\% \text{ uphill slope reduction} = 0.322$$
$$2\% \text{ uphill slope reduction} = 0.644$$

Increased distance required:

$$\frac{160.44^2}{2 \times (5.728 - 0.644)} = 2531.569 \text{ ft} = 771.82 \text{ m}$$

Thus, for a two per cent uphill slope the increase in distance to fifty feet, when compared to a level runway, equals 87 m; or, in terms of factors, the original TODR should be factored by 772/685 = 1.127.

Table 9.3 gives a guide to the factors to be applied for given runway slopes, altitudes and temperatures.

Table 9.3

Aerodrome pressure altitude	1% ← Up-slope → 2%			
	ISA	ISA + 10°C	ISA	ISA + 10°C
sea level	1.06	1.065	1.125	1.14
2000 ft	1.07	1.07	1.14	1.15
4000 ft	1.075	1.08	1.16	1.17
6000 ft	1.085	1.09	1.18	1.195

N.B. The table is a guide only, information contained in the performance document should be used, preferentially. As with Groups C and D, performance effect of a down-sloping runway should be treated as a safety margin.

En-route Requirements

9.7 Regulation 10(1) (c) requires that the aeroplane will — in the expected meteorological conditions, in the event of an engine failure at any point on its route, or any planned diversion therefrom, with the other engine(s) operating within the specified maximum continuous power conditions — be capable of continuing the flight not below the minimum safe altitude (calculated from, or contained in the Operations Manual) to a point 1000 ft above a place at which a safe landing can be made.

In assessing the foregoing, the aeroplane shall not be assumed to be capable of flying at an altitude higher than that at which it is capable of a rate of climb of 150 fpm, with all engines operating within the specified maximum continuous power conditions, and if it is necessary for the aeroplane to be flown by instruments, be capable of a rate of climb of 100 fpm with one engine inoperative.

It is noted that, as with Group D aeroplanes, the requirement of a 150 fpm rate of climb, with all engines operating, defines the net operating ceiling. The data required for determining the net ceiling comprises:

(i) measured 'all engines operating' rates of climb

(ii) measured gliding distance

(iii) measured 'one engine inoperative' rates of climb/descent.

The airspeeds used to establish the above data shall not be less than 1.2Vsl.

The effect of this Regulation is to limit the operation of single-engined aeroplanes on routes on which they are never more than the scheduled gliding distance from a suitable landing place.

9.7.1 Determining net ceiling
Similar to calculating the climb limited weight, this also involves the arithmetical process of proportion, whereby a rate of climb is equated to an altitude difference, which is then used as a correction factor.

The following example, using the data contained in CAP 508, illustrates the method used:

Given an aeroplane weight of 2300 kg, and a temperature of ISA + 15°C, determine the net ceiling.
Difference between maximum weight and actual weight = 2450−2300 = 150 kg.
Thus, rate of climb correction = +135 fpm

At 14,000 ft: ROC = 130 (2450 kg) correction = 135
true rate of climb = 265 fpm
At 16,000 ft: ROC = −35 (2450 kg) correction = 135
true rate of climb = 100 fpm
ROC required = 150 fpm
Difference = 50 fpm

Altitude at which 150 fpm can be sustained:

$$14000 + \frac{2000 \times 115}{165} \text{ or } 16000 - \frac{2000 \times 50}{165} = 15394 \text{ ft}$$

9.7.2   En-route flight path
When calculating the en-route flight path for Group E aeroplanes, the following, simple formulae are acceptable:

(i)   Height gained in feet per nautical mile travelled horizontally;
$$\frac{60 \times \text{rate of climb}}{\text{ground speed}}$$

(ii)   Distance travelled horizontally in nautical miles per 1000 ft height change;
$$\frac{16.67 \times \text{ground speed}}{\text{rate of climb/descent}}$$

In both formulae, ground speed is in knots and rate of climb/descent in fpm.

Landing Requirements

9.8   The landing requirements applicable to Group E aeroplanes are covered by Regulation 10(1) (d) and (e), and are found to be relatively straightforward when compared with the landing requirements of other groups. The requirements for this group are considered under the headings of Landing Climb and Landing Distance.

9.8.1 Landing Climb

Regulation 10(1) (d) requires that the aeroplane's landing weight, at the destination or alternate aerodrome, pressure altitude and expected air temperature, will not exceed the maximum landing weight specified at which:

(i)   the aeroplane is capable, in the en-route configuration with all engines operating within the specified maximum continuous power conditions, of a rate of climb of 700 fpm, if it has retractable landing gear, and 500 fpm, if it has fixed landing gear

(ii) the aeroplane is capable, in the en-route configuration and if it is necessary for it to be flown on instruments for any period after leaving the minimum safe altitude on the last stage of the route flown, (as specified in, or calculated from the Operations Manual relating to the aeroplane) and with one engine inoperative, of a rate of climb of 150 fpm.

Thus, it may be seen that the landing climb limit is predicated on the same criteria as the take-off climb limit, with the calculations pertaining to the landing climb being identical also.

9.8.2 Landing Distance

The landing distance required at the destination or alternate aerodrome must not exceed seventy per cent of the landing distance available on the most suitable runway for landing in still air conditions; the distance required to land from a height of fifty feet (screen height) shall be that appropriate to:

(i)   the landing weight

(ii) the aerodrome pressure altitude

(iii) the temperature in the specified International Standard Atmosphere appropriate to the altitude of the aerodrome — ISA.

The measured landing distance may be defined as the gross horizontal distance required to land on a dry, hard surface from the screen height and come to a complete stop, with all engines operating, and with one engine inoperative. Landing distance data contained in the performance document will usually be the measured distance, unfactored by the regulatory seventy per cent (1.43). Conditions applicable when determining the measured landing distance are shown in Figure 9.4, which also shows the composition of landing distance required; but note, the measured landing distance comprises the airborne distance plus the ground roll.

Figure 9.4
Landing Distance Required — Destination and Alternate Aerodromes

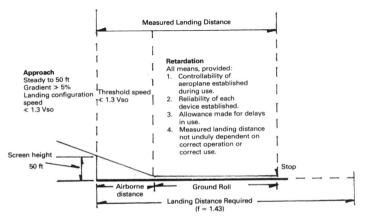

9.9 Determining the Maximum Landing Weight

As with the other performance groups, the field length limited landing weight is obtained by matching the distance available to the distance required. However, remembering that the performance document only lists distances appropriate to the maximum allowable weight, some correction will be required for weights less than the maximum. Also, since the measured distance is unfactored, it will be necessary to factorise the distance available by the regulatory 1.43, in order to compare 'like with like'. The resulting difference in distance is then equated to a weight correction to be applied to the maximum weight. Note that no consideration is required for runway slope or wind component (but see Table 9.5).

Using the data contained in CAP 508, the following example is given as a guide to the method used:

Aerodrome pressure altitude = 2500 ft
Declared landing distance available (dry and paved) = 900 m
Effective landing distance available = 900/1.43 = 629 m
Landing distance required at 2450 kg = 658 m
Difference = 29 m
Difference: 15 m = 100 kg
Difference of 29 m = 193 kg
Thus, the field length limited landing weight = 2450 − 193 = 2257 kg.

The field length limited landing weight is then compared to the climb limited weight, where selection of the more restrictive (lower) weight will provide the maximum permitted landing weight for the aerodrome.

9.10 Landing — grass runways

As with the measured take-off distance, the measured landing distance will have been taken on a dry, hard (paved) surface. Landing on a grass runway will entail the measured landing distance being incremented or factored, the amount being dependent on the state and length of the grass.

Information relating to the factors to be applied should be contained in the performance document but, as with take-off, the advisory factors can only be considered as the minimum acceptable.

Table 9.5 can be used as a guide on the factors to be applied, not only for grass runways, but for other variables also.

9.11 Runway slope and wind

Table 9.5 includes the factors to be applied when accounting for runway slope and wind component. In the case of the former, only a downhill slope is considered, since it increases the landing distance required; it would be prudent therefore to take this into account. Any decrease in the landing distance required because of an uphill slope should be ignored and treated as a safety margin. In the case of wind component, a tailwind only is considered, since it increases the landing distance required (take-off distance also). In ninety-degree cross-winds, the main problem may well be that of handling, depending on wind strength.

Table 9.5

Condition	Take-off Increase in distance to height 50 ft.	(f)	Landing Increase in distance from 50 ft.	(f)
10% increase in aeroplane weight	20%	1.2	10%	1.1
Increase of 1000 ft in aerodrome altitude	10%	1.1	5%	1.05
Increase of 10°C in ambient temperature	10%	1.1	5%	1.05
Dry grass — short 5″	20%	1.2	20%	1.2
long 5-10″	25%	1.25	30%	1.3
Wet grass — short long	25% 30%	1.25 1.3	30% 40%	1.3 1.4
2% slope	uphill 10%	1.1	downhill 10%	1.1
Tailwind component of 10% of lift-off speed	20%	1.2	20%	1.2
Soft ground or snow	25% or more	1.25 +	25% or more	1.25 +
Regulatory factors	—	1.33	—	1.43

In the cases of dry and wet grass, and slope, the effect on the ground roll will be greater.
Factors are cumulative and must be multiplied.

APPENDICES

Appendix 1 outlines the basis for the requirements related to Extended Range Twin Operations (ETOPS), whereas the subsequent appendices illustrate the application of the principles outlined in the Performance Document.

However, before studying the given examples (which involve extensive use of CAP 385), it must be noted that the requirements outlined in Section 6 of this book are based on JAR 25; whilst the airworthiness requirements, and consequently the scheduled performance data of CAP 385, are based on BCAR, Section D. In the context of this book, the differences between the two sets of requirements are considered to be insignificant.

In some of the following examples, use has been made of the examples published in CAP 385; these will be annotated accordingly and, where a specific performance chart is used, it will be referred to as per CAP (eg Figure 16), whereas reference to a diagram will be to that contained in the appendix, or the body of the book.

Where a published example is used, the primary calculations and/or conclusions thereof will not always be included but, in all cases dealing with Performance Group A aeroplane problems, the data presented will be processed by using the scheduled performance data of CAP 385. Readers will be expected to consult the CAP references, as given.

Appendix 1

Extended Range Twin Operations (ETOPS)

1. The purpose of this appendix is to familiarise the reader with the development, purpose, concept, considerations, terminology, and the related requirements and legislation associated with ETOPS. Readers requiring a study in more depth should refer to CAP 513.

2. **Development**
    With the introduction of the advanced turbo-fan engine, powering the larger, twin-engined transport aeroplanes, it became possible for these 'twins' to operate in long range sectors that hitherto had been the province of the larger, three- or four-engined transports only, and in the past, where it was necessary for regulatory bodies to consider only the larger aeroplanes when recommending safe operating standards and practices, it became necessary to include twin-engined aeroplanes.

    One of the problems to be taken into account when planning long-range flights is the availability of suitable aerodromes where a landing can be made in the event of an emergency; additional problems associated with the loss of engine power, or certain major airframe systems on a 'twin', make it necessary at the outset to set a limit on the distance a 'twin' may be from an adequate aerodrome without special requirements being imposed. This distance will be equal to sixty minutes' still air flying time, at the normal 'one engine inoperative' cruise speed. Any planned operation involving a twin-engined, public transport aeroplane beyond this distance from an adequate aerodrome, will be considered an Extended Range Operation.

    The sixty-minute threshold was based on the following:

    (i)   a maximum time compatible with the system capabilities of most existing 'twins', unless incorporating manufacturer's options to improve integrity

    (ii) it is appropriate for new aeroplanes fitted with new engines not having reached maturity

    (iii) an acceptable threshold already existing in the legislation of some states

(v) a threshold beyond which the current experience of 'twins' is very limited.

CAP 513 outlines the criteria by which ETOPS will be assessed and, if approved, it will be authorised by a variation of the Air Operators Certificate (AOC).

When determining the requirements for ETOPS it was evident that some existing three- or four-engined aeroplanes fell short of the requirements. However, the Authority believes that all aeroplanes should comply with similar requirements for long range operations and intends, in due course, to propose changes to legislation of requirements.

3. **Terminology**

Extended Range Operations.
These are operations intended to be, or are actually conducted over, a route that contains a point further than sixty minutes' still air flying time at the normal 'one engine inoperative' cruise speed, from an adequate aerodrome; alternatively, when the threshold distance has been agreed with the Authority. All non-ETOPS flights shall remain within the threshold distance.

Threshold Distance.
The distance travelled in sixty minutes by an aeroplane after engine failure, flying at the speed, power setting and flight level agreed with the Authority and specified in the Operations Manual.
Threshold time: sixty minutes.

Adequate Aerodrome.
An aerodrome which the operator considers to be adequate, having regard to Article 27(1) (c) of the ANO and Regulations 7 and 15 of the AN(G)R. In particular, it should be expected that at the anticipated time of use:

(i) the aerodrome will be available and equipped with necessary ancillary services (ATC, sufficient lighting, communications, weather reporting, navigation aids and safety cover)

(ii) at least one let-down aid (ground radar would qualify) will be available for an instrument approach.

Suitable Aerodrome.

A suitable aerodrome is an adequate aerodrome where (at the anticipated time of use) weather reports, forecasts, or a combination thereof indicate that the weather conditions are very likely to be at, or above, the normal operating minima, using the criteria as set out in CAP 513.

ETOPS Segment.

The portion of an ETOPS flight that begins when the aeroplane is more than the threshold distance from an adequate aerodrome, and ends at the latest time the aeroplane is more than the threshold distance from an adequate aerodrome.

Normal 'One Engine Inoperative' Cruise Speed.

The TAS specified in the ETOPS Airworthiness Approval of the Aeroplane Flight Manual, or agreed with the Authority and specified in the Operations Manual. If not specified, it shall be calculated from the single-engine cruise control data, assuming that:

(i)   the aeroplane take-off weight is at the maximum authorised

(ii) the aeroplane climbs to and maintains the twin-engined optimum initial cruise level for long-range cruise, in ISA conditions, until two hours from take-off

(iii) at its then current weight, in ISA conditions, with one engine inoperative and the other engine at the power recommended, it is flying level at a comfortably acheivable height.

Rule Time.

The maximum diversion time that any point on the route may be from a suitable aerodrome for landing, as specified by the Authority and included in the Operations Manual.

Rule Distance.

The distance travelled in still air in the rule time by an aeroplane, after shutting down one engine in the normal cruise, and flying at the speed, power setting and flight level agreed with the Authority and specified in the

Operations Manual, being the greatest distance that an aeroplane may be from a suitable aerodrome for landing.

4. **Purpose and Applicability**
   CAP 513 states an acceptable means — but not the only means — by which approval may be given for UK-registered, twin-engined aeroplanes in respect of ETOPS. The detailed requirements of the CAP will be applicable to all twin-engined aeroplanes (including those powered by turbo-propellers and reciprocating engines) which are flying for the purpose of public transport, and which meet the following criteria:

   (i)   the maximum take-off weight exceeds 5700 kg

   (ii) the aeroplane is certified to carry more than nineteen passengers.

   Many of the requirements of the CAP are incorporated into an operator's approval for other aeroplanes and route structures. However, ETOPS necessitates the re-evaluation of these approvals to ensure that a level of safety, broadly consistent with that for three- or four-engined aeroplanes, also applies to 'twins'.

   To be eligible for ETOPS, the specified airframe/engine combination, type design considerations, in service experience, and the continuing airworthiness and operations aspects must all be taken into account. Approval of ETOPS will be on a case-by-case basis and may be conditional.

5. **Concepts and Considerations**
   Although it is apparent that the overall safety of an extended range operation cannot be better than that provided by engine reliability, other factors (eg cargo compartment fire suppression/containment capability, operational practices invalidating certain assumptions made during type design certification, or the probability of systems failures) could prove to cause more significant problems. Thus, although engine reliability is a critical factor, it is not the only factor which should be considered when evaluating ETOPS.

   Consideration should also be given to the probability of any condition inhibiting the continued safe flight and a landing occurring, as well as any condition which reduces aeroplane capability, or the crew's ability to cope with adverse operating conditions. With that in mind, it follows that the type design certification of an aeroplane is such that the design of the systems assessed is acceptable for the safe conduct of the intended operation.

In the case of engines it is necessary that, to maintain a level of safety comparable with that achieved by other long-range aeroplanes, all twin-engined aeroplanes used in ETOPS should have an acceptable low risk of double-engine failure for all design and operations related causes. Also, in the event of a single-engine failure, the performance and reliability of the airframe systems, and the operative engine, should be such as to ensure a high probability of continued safe flight and landing. Flight crew workload and procedures in relation to systems failures or malfunction will be reviewed in respect of ETOPS, the normal certification assessment being examined to ensure that exceptional piloting skills, or crew co-ordination are not required.

An in-depth review will also be made of training programmes, operations and maintenance programmes, in the interest of maintaining an acceptable level of systems reliability.

6. **Aeroplane Performance Data**
    No aeroplane should be despatched on an extended range flight unless the Operations Manual contains:

    (a) detailed 'one engine inoperative' performance data, covering
         (i)   drift-down
         (ii)   cruise
         (iii) holding
         (iv)   altitude capability
         (v)   missed approach

    (b) details of any other conditions relevant to extended-range operations which can cause a significant deterioration of performance (eg ice accretion, or ram air turbine deployment).

7. **Operational Limitations**
    The main aspect of these limitations concerns the area of operations for which the operator will be approved, being

specified in the AOC, and the Operators' instructions contained in the Flight Manual.

(a) Area of operation.
Authority may be granted to conduct ETOPS with a particular airframe/engine combination, within an area where the maximum diversion time from any point along the proposed route, to an adequate aerodrome, is 120 minutes or less (as specified by the Authority) at the normal 'one engine inoperative' cruise speed, in ISA conditions and still air.

(b) Operations Manual Instructions.
For planning purposes, instructions should specify the maximum diversion time from a suitable aerodrome, and the criteria by which that maximum diversion time is determined, ie the use of:

(i) standard maximum diversion time

(ii) increased maximum diversion time.

In the former, instructions should ensure that ETOPS are limited to flight plan routes where a maximum diversion time of 120 minutes, or less, to a suitable aerodrome can be met. In the latter, subject to CAA approval, the Operations Manual could provide for an increase of up to fifteen per cent in maximum diversion time from a suitable aerodrome, provided that the aeroplane is never more than 120 minutes from an adequate aerodrome, in the same conditions.

This additional approval is gained by establishing the following:

(i) special maintenance practices and procedures

(ii) special operating practices and procedures

(iii) special crew training

(iv) special equipment.

Operations Manual instructions should also include those procedures to be adopted by the pilot in the event of an engine shut-down, and/or in the event of a single or multiple primary system failure. Contingency procedures or plans should not be interpreted in any way which prejudices the final authority and responsibility of the pilot-in-command for the safe operation of the aeroplane.

N.B. The limitations given above, specifically that relating to allowable distance from a suitable alternate has recently (May 1990) been amended; the distance is increased from the given 120 minutes plus fifteen per cent, to 180 minutes at the one engine inoperative cruise speed. Other relevant requirements relating to engine time and operational experience has also been amended.

8. Related Legislation and Requirements

ANO

Article 6: Provisions in respect of the issue and terms therein of the AOC.

Article 27: Operators' responsibilities relating to en-route navigation aids, suitability of aerodromes, and crewing standards.

Article 29: Public transport operating conditions relating to the aeroplane's weight and performance, as contained in the C of A, and aeroplane capability following engine failure.

Article 32: Pre-flight action by the aeroplane commander.

Schedule 5: Aeroplane scale of equipment.

AN(G)R

7: Weight and performance requirements of public transport aeroplanes classified in Group A.

15: Aerodrome facilities in respect of approach to and landing, for aeroplanes flying for the purpose of public transport.

JAR

25.901: Engine installation, including components that affect control of the engine and engine safety, between the normal inspections and overhauls.

25.903: Type certification of engines; engine isolation so that failure of any engine or any system affecting the engine, will not prevent the continued safe operation of the remaining engine(s). The engine(s) must have a re-start capability within a specified airspeed envelope, also, electrical power for engine ignition must be from an independent source.

25.1309: Equipment, systems and installations which, required by JAR, must be such that their intended functions are performed under any foreseeable conditions so that failure, which would prevent a continued safe flight and landing, is extemely remote.

AOC

Part 1: Operation of aircraft.

Part 2: Arrangements for engineering support.

Appendix 2

V1/VR Range
Reference Cap 385, p.17 — Selection of V1

The concept of a V1/VR range being available to determine a decision speed (V1) for take-off also becomes an important factor in other performance aspects, notably the determination of a maximum permitted take-off weight and associated V1 when the normal procedure produces a V1 in excess of the Brake Energy Limiting Speed (Vmbe). The use of a 'high' or 'low' V1 can also affect the true take-off and emergency distances required for a given take-off weight. Before studying these aspects, the basis for such a range should be considered.

The occasions on which a V1/VR range becomes available has been given in 6.4, and the method of determination outlined in the CAP reference given above. The following example and associated diagram 2.1 illustrates a normal take-off weight calculation, with the actual or planned take-off weight being somewhat less than both the field length and WAT limited take-off weights.

Example 1

Aerodrome pressure altitude:	sea level
OAT:	10°C
TORA:	2400 m
EDA:	2500 m
TODA:	2600 m
Runway slope:	Nil
Reported wind component:	Nil
Tyre speed rating:	225 mph
ACS packs:	Off

Calculations:

Runway length correction — all engines operating	(Fig 8): 2600 m
Emergency distance correction	(Fig 9): 2500 m
Runway length correction — one engine inoperative	(Fig 11): 2505 m
	V1/VR: 0.90
Limiting distance D: one engine inoperative	(Fig 11)

Maximum take-off weight — field
   length limited   (Fig 12): 191,000 kg
WAT limited take-off weight   (Fig 14): 212,500 kg
Tyre speed limit   (Fig 15): 240,000 kg
Maximum permitted take-off weight: 191,000 kg

Take-off speeds (all speeds in knots IAS)
   Fig 16 V1/VR   = 0.90
   V1 wet   = 137.5
   V1 dry   = 148.5
   VR   = 152.5
   V2   = 160
   Vmcg   = 115.5
   Brake energy speed (Fig 17):   171

Diagram 2.1

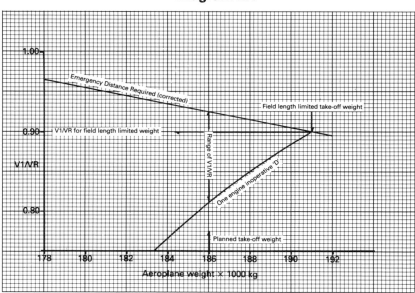

Diagram 2.1 has been constructed on the basis of the method used in the given CAP reference and shows the weight–V1/VR relationship of the 'one engine inoperative' distance D and the corrected emergency distance required. It will be noted that it is similar to the field analysis graphs given in 6.16, 6.17 and 6.18 but, in this case, only the effective parameters have been plotted. It may also be noted that the diagram is a compound version of figures 11 and 12/13 of CAP 385.

In the diagram, where the 'one engine inoperative' distance D is intersected by the corrected emergency distance, the field length limited take-off weight and associated V1/VR is given, in this case 191,000 kg and 0.90, respectively. Assuming the take-off was made at the given weight and using the corresponding V1/VR, and that an engine failure occurred at the V1/VR (which in this case corresponds to a V1 dry of 148.5 kt), then the requirements pertaining to take-off and emergency distances in the event of continuing or abandoning the take-off would be satisfied, or the maximum distances would be used in either case. It is therefore logical to assume, that if the take-off was made at a lesser weight, something less than the distances at maximum weight would be required. To go one step further, if the calculated V1/VR of 0.90 was used at any weight below the maximum permitted, the distances required to reach either the screen height at V2, or that required to stop may well be less than those available.

Assuming a planned, or actual, take-off weight of 186,000 kg (Fig 12 gives the distance D required as 2360 m) the diagram shows that at this weight a V1/VR range of 0.812 to 0.925 becomes available for use. (The values given may be confirmed using Fig 11 with the distance D required.) Thus, the actual take-off weight of 186,000 kg, at the aerodrome and ambient conditions given, the V1/VR range, when converted to speeds, gives:

	V1 wet	V1 dry
Minimum	122 kt	133 kt
Maximum	139 kt	150 kt

Thus, for the actual take-off weight, assuming dry runway conditions, any V1 dry between 133 and 150 (subject to VR) may be selected and used in the knowledge that, should an engine failure occur at the selected V1, distance requirements would be met thereby inferring a safe operation. It may also be deduced from the diagram that, assuming that the 'low' V1 dry was used, an engine failure at that speed would entail use of the full distance D required at the weight, if the take-off was continued, whilst if the take-off was abandoned, something much less than the full emergency distance required at the weight would be needed. Conversely, if the 'high' V1 was used, the opposite would apply. Bearing in mind the definition of V1, the distances required appropriate to the V1/VR used (which may be confirmed again in Figure 11) are as follows:

	TOD	**ED**
Low V1/VR	2600 m	1880 m
High V1/VR	2360 m	2500 m

This particular aspect of the take-off distance required becomes an important element of obstacle clearance, involving a sloping runway where the full amount of take-off distance available cannot be used.

Diagram 2.2 is based on the data of Example 1 of CAP 385, and constructed on the same basis as 2.1. In 2.2, where the maximum permitted take-off weight is limited by the WAT limit of 188,700 kg, the V1/VR range for this weight extends from 0.85 to 0.952 which, when converted to speeds (V1) gives:

	V1 wet	**V1 dry**
Minimum	130 kt	141 kt
Maximum	145.5 kt	155.5 kt
		reduce to VR = 153

By substituting the WAT limited weight with the maximum structural weight (195,000 kg), with the field length limit in

Diagram 2.2

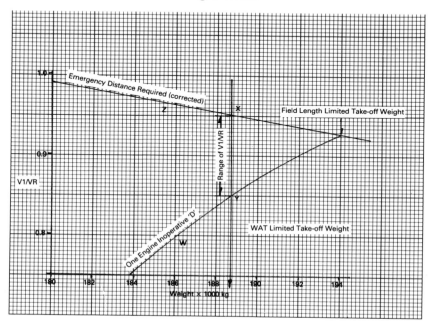

excess of this, it can be seen that, even at the maximum weight authorised, it is possible to obtain a range of V1/VR.

Diagram 2.2 also shows that for a further reduced weight, say, 186,000 kg, the V1/VR range is extended further (points W and Z) to 0.80 and 0.964, proving that, as the difference between the maximum permitted and the actual/planned take-off weights increase, the V1/VR range also increases.

Appendix 3

Take-off weight limited by Vmbe
Reference CAP 385 p.17 — Selection of V1
V1 greater than Vmbe

Determining the minimum V1 available for use is an important factor in calculating the maximum permitted take-off weight, when the V1 calculated in the normal procedure proves to be in excess of the Vmbe for the same weight. Under such conditions a number of options are available to the assessor:

(i)   Reduce the V1 to be used to the minimum permitted for the weight (with a lower limit corresponding to a V1/VR of 0.76). Should the V1 still prove to be in excess of Vmbe then,

(ii)   reduce take-off weight, which has the dual effect of lowering the minimum V1 available and increasing the Vmbe. When take-off weight needs to be reduced, it is usual to utilize

(iii)   a combination of (i) and (ii).

Option (i) is illustrated in Diagram 3.1 and based on the following:

Example 1

Aerodrome pressure altitude:	5000 ft
OAT:	+20°C
TORA:	3900 m
EDA:	3950 m
TODA:	4000 m
Runway Slope:	0.5% down
Reported wind component:	5 kt tail
Tyre speed rating:	225 mph
ACS packs:	Off

It may be noted that both the WAT limit and Vmbe are affected by common factors, eg hot, high-altitude aerodromes. However, Vmbe is also adversely affected by a down-sloping runway with a tailwind component.

Calculations:

Runway length correction — all engines operating	(Fig 8): 3870 m
Emergency distance correction	(Fig 9): 3620 m
Runway length correction — one engine inoperative	(Fig 11): 3650 m
	V1/VR: 0.915
Limiting distance D:	3650 m
Maximum take-off weight — field length limited	(Fig 13): 191,700 kg
WAT limited weight	(Fig 14): 186,500 kg
Tyre speed limit	(Fig 15): 212,000 kg
Maximum permitted take-off weight:	186,500 kg
	WAT limited.

Take-off speeds — knots IAS (Fig 16):

V1 wet:	=	139
V1 dry:	=	150
VR:	=	152
V2:	=	157
Vmbe — 186,500 kg — (Fig 17)		145

Since V1dry>Vmbe, determine minimum V1 at WAT limit.

Fig 13 At 186,500 kg distance D required	= 3430 m
Fig 11 Minimum V1/VR at 186,500 kg	= 0.835
Minimum V1	= 140 kt
Thus, Maximum permitted take-off weight	= 186,500 kg
V1:	140 kt
Vmbe:	145 kt

Therefore, by using the minimum V1 available the calculated maximum permitted take-off weight of 186,500 kg need not be reduced and, as shown in the calculations, there is in fact a small range of decision speeds available, even though they are limited by Vmbe. However, in such cases it would be prudent and expedient to use the low V1, as calculated.

Diagram 3.1 illustrates the results of the calculations made in the example, and shows quite clearly the relationship between the original V1/VR at the field length limit, the equivalent V1/VR of the Vmbe and the minimum V1/VR, all for the WAT limited take-off weight.

Diagram 3.1

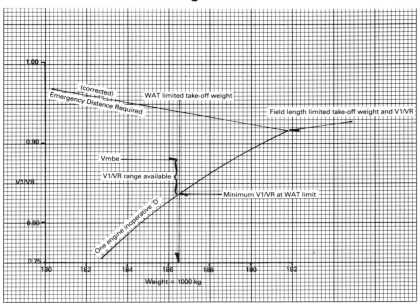

Example 2

Aerodrome pressure altitude:	4000 ft
OAT:	+22°C
TORA:	3650 m
EDA:	3800 m
TODA:	4050 m
Runway slope:	1.0% down
Reported wind component:	10 kt tail
Tyre speed rating:	225 mph
ACS packs:	Off

Calculations:

Fig 8 All engines operating:	3760 m
Fig 9 Emergency distance:	3140 m
Fig 11 One engine inoperative:	3480 m
V1/VR:	0.875
Fig 13 Field limited take-off weight:	193,000 kg
Fig 14 WAT limited take-off weight:	191,500 kg
Fig 15 Tyre speed limit:	Not limiting
Maximum permitted take-off weight:	191,500 kg

Fig 16 Take-off speeds (kts IAS).
  V1 wet   = 135

V1 dry = 146
VR   = 154
V2   = 158.5
Fig 17 Vmbe (191,500 kg)   136.5

V1>Vmbe
Minimum V1/VR at 191,500 kg
Fig 13 Distance D at 191,500 kg: 3440 m
Fig 11 Minimum V1/VR: 0.855
Fig 16 Minimum V1:   143

Minimum V1>Vmbe. Take-off weight must be reduced. For the specimen aeroplane the factor used to reduce weight is given as 500 kg/kt difference between V1 and Vmbe.

Difference = 6.5 × 500 = 3250 kg.

Vmbe limited take-off weight = 191,500−3250 = 188,250 kg.

The performance data of the specimen aeroplane also requires the V1 to be set at the Vmbe.

Thus: V1 dry = 136.5, VR = 152, V2 = 157 kt IAS.

Diagram 3.2 illustrates the foregoing calculations and shows the relationship of the minimum V1/VR at the WAT limited weight; the equivalent V1/VR of the Vmbe at the same weight;

Diagram 3.2

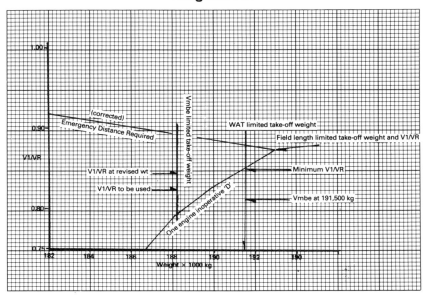

the corresponding V1/VR to be used at the Vmbe limited take-off weight; and the corresponding V1/VR of the Vmbe at the same weight. In the diagram it may be seen that applying the weight factor, and setting V1 to Vmbe has the effect of lowering the weight and thus increasing the Vmbe — at the reduced weight — and lowering the corresponding V1/VR of the V1 to be used, so that it lies well within the take-off and emergency distances' requirement parameters.

Having calculated a reduced (Vmbe limited) take-off weight, it will be necessary to determine a VR and V2 for the revised weight; the V1 has been set at the original restricting Vmbe and, though the effect of weight reduction is to increase the Vmbe, it is not necessary to determine a new Vmbe.

It should be noted at this pont that the procedures used above are peculiar to the specimen aeroplane only. Other Performance Group A aeroplanes' procedures may differ, but it may generally be found that the principles involved in solving the foregoing problem(s) are basically the same for all aeroplanes.

Appendix 4

Variable Thrust Take-off
Reference CAP 385 Appendix 1

Variable or reduced thrust take-off was developed mainly in the interest of conserving engine life; prior to development, maximum take-off thrust was used on all departures, regardless of aeroplane weight or field length available. The use of reduced thrust has enhanced engine life and, equally important, improved engine reliability.

In the procedure the thrust required for take-off is predicated on an 'assumed temperature', usually higher than ambient, and determined by a combination of aeroplane weight, aerodrome characteristics, and ambient conditions. The thrust so used from the calculations is such that, if the assumed temperature existed, it would be the maximum take-off thrust at that temperature. The procedure may only be used when full thrust is not needed to meet the performance requirements of the take-off and initial climb, and may be used at the commander's discretion.

Before allowing the procedure to be put into practice the operator must gain approval from the CAA's Safety Regulation Group, and provide all the information necessary — including a worked example — in the aeroplane's Flight Manual. The procedure must also include a method whereby the engines are monitored, periodically checking that full thrust is available at any time. Subsequent to approval, an operator may require the procedure to be carried out, providing that the safety aspects are not compromised.

Take-off can be limited by many considerations, as outlined in Section 6, but for variable thrust the most significant are:

(a) Take-off field length(s)

(b) WAT limit (climb gradient)

(c) Maximum thrust reduction

(d) Net take-off flight path (obstacle clearance).

Structural limits notwithstanding, the maximum permitted take-off weight is usually determined by one of (a), (b) and (d).

However, where the actual take-off weight is such that none of them is limiting, thrust may be reduced until one of (a) to (d) becomes limiting. The usual method used to determine the thrust required to meet the limitations imposed is the 'assumed temperature' principle. All other parameters maintaining actual values, a temperature (higher than ambient) is determined at which the actual take-off weight equals the field length limited weight, the WAT limited weight, or the obstacle limited weight; or the temperature determined may equal that for the maximum thrust reduction permitted.

Method

(a) Take-off field length

Where a given field length would provide a maximum take-off weight at the ambient temperature, with the field length remaining constant, as temperature increases take-off weight decreases. Thus for a given pressure altitude, field length and take-off weight, there is an 'upper' temperature above which the field length becomes limiting. This 'upper' temperature becomes the field length limiting temperature at the actual take-off weight.

Let this temperature be T_1.

(b) WAT limit

Similar to field length in (a) above, for a given pressure altitude and temperature the WAT curve will give the highest aeroplane weight at which the climb gradient(s) can be met; or, for the given gradients, as weight is reduced the temperature appropriate to the required gradients increases (eg for a given pressure altitude and aeroplane weight there is a temperature above which the required minimum gradients would not be met). The WAT curve or graph is used to determine this limiting temperature.

Let this temperature be T_2.

(c) Maximum thrust reduction

For all Performance Group A aeroplanes approved to practise this procedure there is an airworthiness imposed maximum acceptable thrust reduction, which may either be expressed in EPR or percentage engine RPM. For the specimen aeroplane the maximum thrust reduction is 0.057 EPR. To calculate the minimum thrust permitted for take-off and its corresponding temperature, first the maximum thrust at the ambient temperature is determined. This is then diminished by the maximum thrust reduction allowed -0.057 — thus giving the minimum permissible thrust. Remembering that thrust decreases as temperature increases, the higher temperature corresponding to the minimum thrust at the given pressure altitude is then determined. This is the temperature above which the use of minimum thrust would not be permitted.

Let this temperature be T_3.

These three take-off parameters are usually the most limiting criteria of the reduced thrust procedure; the maximum assumed temperature that may be used to calculate reduced thrust being the **lowest** of T_1, T_2 and T_3.

It should be evident at this stage that the performance factor that may have been limiting at full thrust, eg WAT limit, need not be a limiting factor at reduced thrust.

Having determined the maximum assumed temperature that may be used, selection of the assumed temperature to be used would depend on the operator's procedures but, providing the temperature selected for use lies between the ambient and the maximum assumed temperature and is within the aeroplane's environmental envelope, it is acceptable. The usual practice is to use the maximum assumed temperature calculated.

(d) Obstacle clearance
If obstacles are present within the NTOFP area, obstacle clearance should be checked using the selected assumed temperature. If the obstacles are not cleared, a lower assumed temperature should be determined by using the appropriate obstacle clearance chart(s), in conjunction with the take-off climb gradient chart. The assumed temperature at which the obstacles are cleared becomes the maximum assumed temperature on which to base thrust calculations.

Take-off speeds
V1, VR and V2 should all be determined using the selected assumed temperature, the V1 by using the V1/VR appropriate to the original (full thrust) take-off weight analysis. The V1 so determined must equal or

exceed Vmcg, which is determined using the ambient temperature since for a given altitude, Vmcg decreases with increase in temperature. Thus, if Vmcg is determined using the maximum assumed temperature, it would result in a critical speed too low for actual conditions. Should V1 be less than Vmcg, using the selected assumed temperature, determine the maximum V1/VR (and thus V1) that may be used; if the V1 is still less than Vmcg, the take-off is field-length limited at the selected assumed temperature, and therefore reduced thrust cannot be scheduled at the selected temperature. A lower temperature should be selected or determined and, if the resulting V1 from the maximum V1/VR exceeds Vmcg, reduced thrust may be scheduled at the lower temperature, whilst making V1 = Vmcg.

Vmbe and tyre speed limitations should be checked using the selected assumed temperature and, if found to be limiting, a new assumed temperature should be determined.

The following examples and asssociated diagrams illustrate the method and principles involved in the procedure.

Example 1

Aerodrome pressure altitude:	1000 ft
OAT:	+20°C
TORA:	2800 m
EDA:	3000 m
TODA:	3100 m
Runway slope:	Nil
Reported wind component:	Nil
Tyre speed rating:	225 mph
ACS packs:	Off

Calculations:

Fig 8 All engines operating:	3100 m
Fig 9 Corrected emergency distance:	3000 m
Fig 11 One engine inoperative:	2990 m
V1/VR:	0.923
Fig 12 Field limited take-off weight:	198,500 kg
Fig 14 WAT limited weight:	207,000 kg
Fig 15 Tyre speed limit:	Not limiting
Maximum permitted take-off weight:	195,000 kg (structural)
Planned take-off weight:	185,000 kg

Determining assumed temperature

(i) Field length limit.
Distance D available   = 2990 m
At 185,000 kg (Figure 13) = +36.5°C
Note that Figure 13 is used and **not** Figure 12. By using the latter, extrapolation would be required as the temperature found would be in excess of +30°C, which is the maximum for use in that Figure. Normally, use of Figures 12/13 is determined by the temperature validity graphs, which should always be observed. However, in this case the validity graphs are not applicable, as a limiting temperature for the take-off weight and distance D is to be determined.

$$T_1 = + 36.5°C$$

(ii) WAT limit.
Figure 14.
At a weight of 185,000 kg the maximum temperature at which the required climb gradient(s) can be sustained is given as

$$+41°C = T_2$$

(iii) Maximum power reduction.
Figure 4.
Normal maximum power at pressure altitude and ambient temperature   = 1.539 EPR
Maximum power reduction   = 0.057

Thus, minimum power: 1.539−0.057 = 1.482 EPR

Temperature appropriate to 1.482 at pressure altitude =

$$+40°C = T_3$$

Maximum assumed temperature that may be used = + 36.5°C.
Temperature is checked within the environmental range.
    EPR at +36.5°C = 1.496 EPR (ACS packs off).

Take-off speeds (Fig 16).
Using 185,000 kg +36.5°C, V1/VR 0.923
V1 wet   = 140.5
V1 dry   = 151.5 (reduce to 151)

$$\begin{aligned}
\text{VR} &= 151\\
\text{V2} &= 156\\
\text{Vmcg at } +20°C &= 114
\end{aligned}$$

Figure 15 Tyre speed limit at +36.5°C (not limiting)
Fig 17 Vmbe at +36.5°C = 163

Diagram 4.1 is a field analysis and illustrates the foregoing example. It shows that, because of the temperature selected for use, the actual take-off weight now becomes the field length limited weight, and where originally the take-off weight was limited by the structural weight, the field length limit is now the limiting parameter. The diagram shows that the originally calculated V1/VR remains valid in the procedure, even though the plotted distance appears to have decreased. Note also, that even when the take-off weight is limited by the structural weight, as in the original calculations, there is still a range of V1/VR available.

Diagram 4.1

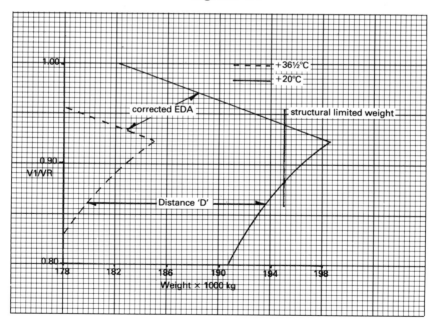

Example 2

Aerodrome pressure altitude:	2000 ft
OAT:	+20°C

TORA: 3000 m
EDA: 3100 m
TODA: 3200 m
Runway slope: 0.5% down
Reported wind component: Nil
Tyre speed rating: 225 mph
ACS packs: Off

Calculations:

Limiting distance D   = 3150 (one engine inoperative)
$V1/VR$ = 0.908
Fig 12 Field limited take-off weight: 197,500 kg
Fig 14 WAT limited take-off weight: 202,000 kg
Fig 15 Tyre speed limit: not limiting
Maximum permitted take-off weight: 195,000 kg (structural)
Planned take-off weight: 178,000 kg

Field limiting temperature
Fig 13 D = 3150 @ 178,000 kg $T_1 = +40°C$

WAT limiting temperature.
Fig 14 178,000 kg @ 2000 ft $T_2 = +40°C$

Minimum EPR
Fig 4
Maximum EPR: 1.546
Maximum reduction: 0.057
Minimum EPR: 1.489

At 1.489 and 2000 ft $T_3 = +38°C$
Maximum assumed and selected temperature $= +38°C$
EPR at selected temperature $= 1.489$

Take-off speeds (Fig 16)
    V1 wet   = 135
    V1 dry   = 146
    VR   = 148.5
    V2   = 153
Vmcg at +20°C = 113
Fig 15 Tyre speed limits: Not limiting
Fig 17 Vmbe: = 163

Initially in example 2, the maximum permitted take-off weight
was limited by the field length available, giving 197,500 kg
(structural weight notwithstanding). The limiting parameter
subsequent to the reduced thrust calculations has now

become the minimum thrust permitted by pressure altitude and temperature — not because of reduced aeroplane weight. In fact, the aeroplane weight would need to be 180,000+ kg before the field length became the limiting factor, in the reduced thrust calculation at +38°C.

Diagram 4.2 illustrates the field analysis for the selected assumed temperature, and it may be noted that, because the field limit is slightly higher than the planned take-off weight, a V1/VR range becomes available. However, this aspect becomes relatively academic as, when using the reduced thrust option, the normal procedure would be to use the V1 corresponding to the original V1/VR determined.

If the planned take-off weight had been 182,000 kg, the limiting parameter would have been the field length limit, in which case only one V1/VR would have been available.

Diagram 4.2

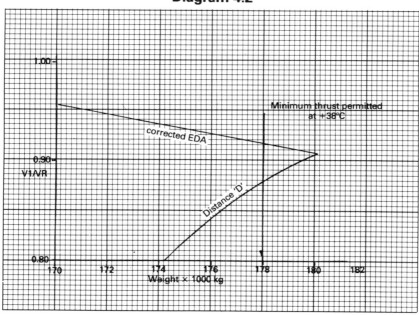

Example 3

Using the data in Example 1 of CAP 385 and, assuming a planned take-off weight of 180,000 kg, the limiting parameter would prove to be the WAT curve at +27.5°C; the field length limit +30°C; and the minimum thrust 1.56−0.057 = 1.503 = +34°C.

In this case the thrust required for take-off would be

1.533−0.01 = 1.523; and the required 'go-around EPR', to account for engine failure, would be 1.547.

Operational Aspects

It has been demonstrated, in the method used, that the reduced thrust used for a take-off is always determined by the most limiting temperature appropriate to its performance parameter. This effectively means that, in the event of a continued take-off after engine failure (after V1) using reduced thrust, the performance requirements minima will still be met, albeit with a small additional margin because of the air density effect of the actual temperature, in comparison with the assumed temperature. However, it is recommended that, under engine failure conditions, thrust on the operating engines should be increased to something approaching full take-off thrust.

The procedural aspect of the reduced thrust take-off requires that one or two engines be 'targetted' (bugged) with the go-round take-off thrust setting, in preparation for engine failure. In practise, full take-off thrust setting is not used, but the go-around EPR for the ambient temperature. The go-around parameter for thrust setting is essentially an airborne setting, predicated on aerodrome pressure altitude and total air temperature (TAT). TAT is usually higher than the ambient temperature, and at aerodrome pressure altitude and typical take-off speeds the difference amounts to approximately two degrees. Thus by using the ambient temperature as TAT, the thrust setting obtained for go-around would be slightly (equivalent to two degrees) less than using the full OAT. In this way, very slightly less than full take-off thrust is obtained but, most importantly, the engines are protected from exceeding their limitations without compromising the safety aspects.

It is also usual to adjust the engines for take-off thrust at an indicated airspeed of forty to eighty knots. This again is to ensure that engine limitations are not exceeded, as above eighty knots the TAT will not indicate true ambient temperature.

It has been stated that there is a mandatory limit to thrust reduction (0.057); this ensures that margins at lower weight take-offs are preserved. Operators may also impose an upper weight limit, beyond which, and up to the RTOW, the reduced thrust procedure may not be used.

Limitations.
(a) Take-off speeds, V1, VR and V2 used must not be less

than those complying with controllability margins, associated with the maximum thrust available for ambient conditions.

(b)   All performance requirements must be met.

(c)   The procedure may not be used:
     (i)   when operating from a contaminated runway
    (ii)   when any non-standard take-off is to be made (eg increased V2 procedure), or a take-off involving the configuration deviation list.

(d)   When operating with a mixed engine configuration.

Appendix 5

The Increased V2 Procedure
Reference CAP 385 pp.10, 11 and 22 Example 3

This procedure will usually be possible at aerodromes where the WAT limit imposes a restriction on the maximum permitted take-off weight. The procedure seeks to obtain a higher maximum allowable take-off weight by using increased take-off speeds which, although increasing the field length(s) required, improves the second-segment climb performance. This improved performance is converted into a relatively small weight increase on the WAT limit. In the case of the specimen aeroplane, this is carried out by comparing the WAT limited weight with the field length limited weight, thus giving an increased permitted take-off weight and an appropriate speed increase.

Diagram 5.1 illustrates, in very general terms, the basic aerodynamic characteristics of an increased V2 — it may be noted that the increased V2 appears to be more aerodynamically efficient than the normal V2 procedure. However, V2 is primarily based on a factor of stall speed (eg V2 = 1.2 Vs) and is thus not necessarily the most aerodynamically efficient at take-off.

The method used to determine the increased weight and speeds is adequately covered in CAP 385; this appendix will outline the operational aspects of the procedure.

Example 3 of CAP 385 utilizes the same aerodrome as Example 1 which, after comparison in Figure 21, gives an increased weight of 190,500 kg, and a speed increase of 1.5%. Subsequently, the take-off speeds are determined using Figure 16. However, to complete the take-off details, flap retraction speeds must be determined. Flap operating speeds are predominantly based on aeroplane weight and the speed associated with that weight. In this case the weight is given as 190,500 kg, and the speed associated with that weight as 158 kt (V2). The flap retraction schedule for the specimen aeroplane dictates flap selection to four degrees, to be initiated at V2 + 20 kt; in this case: 178 kt, and flap 0° at V2 = 60 kt = 218 kt.

The 'all engines operating' take-off climb speed (V4), which is used to the point where acceleration to flap retraction speed is initiated, is related to the V2 used in the procedure, in this case the increased V2. Thus V4 = V2 + 10 kt = 170 kt.

The increased V2 procedure may also be used for obstacle clearance purposes, although a slightly different parameter is used in place of the WAT limit. This is described on page 19 and in Example 6, p.25 of the CAP.

Diagram 5.2 illustrates the relative effect of the increased weight on field lengths and V1/VR range. It is apparent that, even with the increased weight, field length requirements are not compromised but that a smaller V1/VR range would be available. In practical terms it would be acceptable for the original V1/VR to be used to determine V1.

Diagram 5.1

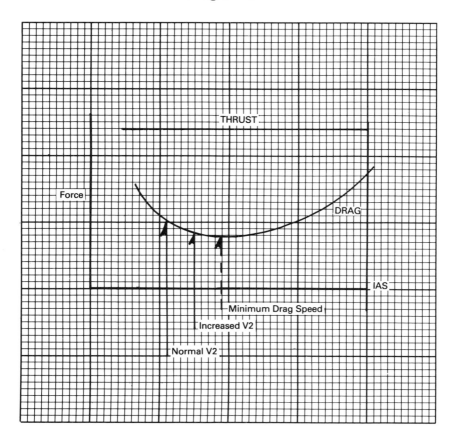

Diagram 5.2

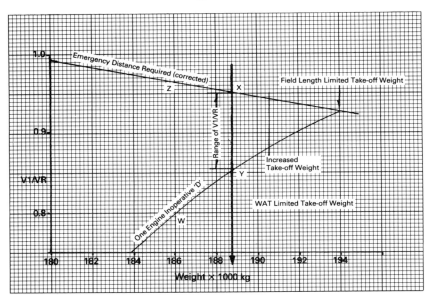

Appendix 6

Obstacle Clearance

The various procedures and the respective methods used in determining obstacle limited take-off weights are adequately covered in CAP 385; this appendix will focus on the more unusual aspects of the various procedures.

(a) **Take-off Climb — Gross Gradient at 400 ft (Fig 18)**
The gross gradient available at 400 ft is extracted from the given figure using, with the other parameters contained therein, the **field length limited take-off weight**. This weight should **always** be used, regardless of it being in excess of either the structural maximum or the WAT limited weights, or both.

The reasons for this are quite straightforward. By definition, the field length limited take-off weight is the maximum weight permitted by the maximum allowable take-off distance — available runway length plus maximum allowable clearway. Thus, in normal circumstances where the whole of the declared TODA is used, reference zero (the end of TODR) may be identified readily as being coincident with the end of TODA.

Obstacle characteristics are usually related to the end of TODA, but obstacle data contained in Figures 19 and 20 are related to reference zero. Therefore, when the whole of TODA is used, obstacle characteristics are directly related to reference zero. Furthermore, the gradient extracted is also related to reference zero, whilst the trade lines are related to the gradients.

Should a weight be less than that prescribed, logically it would entail something less than the maximum usable TOD (TODR<TODA). This being the case, and in order to relate all parameters to a common datum, an adjustment to the obstacle distance would be required. Also, should the TOD involve a slope, obstacle height would require adjustment, to allow for the unused TOD, and the associated higher/lower start point of the flight path (outlined in 6.14). It should also be noted that, prior to using Figure 18, the ambient temperature should be checked on the temperature validity graph. If

a 'false' temperature is required for use, it should be used throughout the entire problem when using Figure 18.

(b) Adjustment of Obstacle Characteristics

6.14 has shown how obstacle characteristics may be affected by changes in TODR, which in turn is dependent on take-off weight. TODR may also be determined by the V1/VR (V1) selected for use, assuming, of course, engine failure occurs at the selected V1. The field length limited take-off weight may be limited by the maximum allowable clearway (eg the 'cut-off lines' in Figures 8 and 11). When this happens, the obstacle characteristics **must** be adjusted. The problem is exemplified as follows:

	Example 1	Example 2
Aerodrome pressure altitude:	3000 ft	50 ft
OAT:	+20°C	+30°C
TORA:	3000 m	2400 m
EDA:	3000 m	3250 m
TODA:	4000 m	3310 m
Runway slope (down):	0.5%	0.65%
Reported wind component:	10 kt (head)	Nil
ACS packs:	On	Off

Obstacle:

Distance from end of TODA:	1400 m	6100 m
Height above end of TODA:	160 ft	1070 ft

In Example 1 the field length limited take-off weight is determined by the 'one engine inoperative' distance D of 3240 m, with a V1/VR of 0.898; the weight being 194,000 kg with the maximum usable TOD, appropriate to the limiting distance D of 3290 m.

Thus there is a difference of 710 m between the maximum usable TOD (TODR) and TODA. Therefore, in relation to reference zero the obstacle is at a distance of 1400 + 710 = 2110 m.

As the TOD involves a slope, obstacle height must be adjusted: 710 m × 3.28 × 0.005 = 12 ft. As the slope is down, the flight path will start higher, decreasing the obstacle height in relation to reference zero. Entry to Figure 19 would be made with the gross gradient available at 400 ft, appropriate to 194,000 kg — obstacle distance 2100 m from reference zero (to be wind corrected), and obstacle height 148 ft.

In Example 2 the field length limited take-off weight is determined by the 'all engines operating' distance D of 2800 m (maximum usable TOD 2700 m). The 'one engine inoperative' distance D, in this case, is 2820 m (maximum usable TOD 2650 m).

Applying the same method as in Example 1, the obstacle distance from reference zero would be calculated as: 3310 − 2700 + 6100 = 6710 m; and the obstacle height would be adjusted to 1070 − (610 × 3.28 × 0.0065) = 1057 ft. Entry to Figure 20 would be with the gross gradient available at 400 ft, appropriate to 193,500 kg; obstacle distance 6710 m (to be wind corrected) and obstacle height 1057 ft.

It should be noted, at this point, that the effective maximum usable TOD, upon which obstacle adjustments are based, is that appropriate to the limiting distance D, and not necessarily the shorter of the two take-off distances required. By following the procedure as outlined, it may be seen that the worst case is considered, as the obstacle is made to appear relatively closer to reference zero.

Regarding the selection of high/low V1/VR and the effect on TODR: if, in Example 1, take-off was made at 190,000 kg it would require a distance D of 3100 m, giving a V1/VR range of 0.842 to 0.911. Assuming that a high V1/VR and its corresponding V1 is used, an engine failure at V1 would entail a TODR of 3120 m; whereas engine failure at a low V1 would entail the use of the entire 3290 m TODR. In this case, the difference between the two distances is considered to be insignificant, as is the result of its application to obstacle height (2.78 ft — insignificant when considering the graticule in use). The main aspect of this case lies in the definition of TODR, as shown in CAP 385, p.4, and the fact that the worst case again is considered.

(c) **Close-in Obstacles (Fig 19)**
Figures 19 and 20 illustrate basically the flight path profiles of the first and second segments, the latter ending at a gross height of 400 ft for all given gradients. However, the corresponding net height will depend on the gradient available (eg at a gross gradient of four per

cent, the second segment should end at a net height of 314 ft (279 + 35 ft), whereas at a gross gradient of five per cent, it should end at a net height of 330 ft).

The field length trade lines are what they imply, lines by which field length is 'traded' for weight. This is done by changing gross gradients until obstacle clearance is achieved and, in so doing, the field length changes in accordance with the change of gradient, which in turn is dependent on take-off weight.

Diagram 6.1 illustrates the procedure, using the data contained in Example 1 of this appendix (the diagram is not to scale). Two reference zeros have been shown to illustrate the change in horizontal distance of the obstacle.

Diagram 6.1

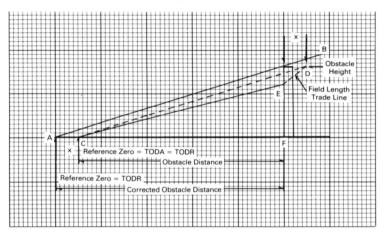

Fig 18 Field length limited take-off weight: 194,000 kg
        'False' temperature: +23°C
        Gross gradient available at 400 ft: 2.55% = CE

Fig 19 Obstacle distance (wind corrected): 2160 m
        Height: 115 ft = E
        Trade line to 148 ft — ED —: = D
        Gradient required — CD —: 2.98%

Since a greater gradient is required, weight is decreased, therefore TODR is decreased.

Decrease in TODR: x
Gradient required: AB // CD
Obstacle distance from 'new'
   reference zero (wind corrected): 2290 m = AF
Difference in distances: 2290−2160=130 m

Change in obstacle height:
130 × 3.28 × 0.005 = 2 ft
Obstacle height decreased to: 146 ft

Trade line to 146 ft — DE —
Gradient required 2.92%

Fig 18 'False' temperature: +23°C
Take-off weight corresponding to
   2.92%: 189,500 kg
Obstacle limited take-off weight: 189,500 kg

It is interesting to note, that in this problem the distances D required for the initial and final take-off weights differ by 160 m, whereas in 'true' TODR the difference is 180 m — the difference being considered insignificant.

(d) Distant Obstacles (Fig 20)

Notwithstanding a small overlap between the gear up point and 400 ft gross height, this figure is a continuation of Figure 19 and is used for obstacle clearance purposes outside the scope of the previous figure; for normal weight reduction problems (eg use of the trade lines) this figure is used in the same manner as Figure 19.

Under normal circumstances an obstacle in the second segment may be cleared by delaying flap retraction (eg an obstacle at 10,000 m — wind corrected — and 900 ft above reference zero) would require a gradient of 3.98%, and delay flap retraction until attaining a gross height of 1230 ft (net 935 ft), in order to clear the obstacle by the required minimum. However, there is a limiting height to which flap retraction may be delayed which, as can be seen in Figure 20, is dependent on the gross gradient (or take-off weight) available at 400 ft; this is given in the figure as the Maximum Level-off Height, and indicates the end of the normal second segment. Basically, it is a function of the five-minute time limit for the use of full take-off power, showing the starting height of the third segment during which the aeroplane is accelerated to flap retraction speed and flaps are fully retracted, all of which must be accomplished within the five minutes allowed from brake release at take-off. This would cover such normal circumstances as an obstacle within the band preceding the maximum level-off height.

Should an obstacle be located beyond the maximum level-off height, and an optimum take-off weight is required, the second-segment climb at V2 may be extended, but, before this can be considered, two important requirements must be met:

(i) the obstacle must be the last in the take-off flight path because performance data relating to third segment distance, using maximum continuous thrust, is unavailable, due to changing aeroplane configuration and speed

(ii) the aeroplane must have a minimum acceleration/climb gradient capability at **all** points in the take-off flight path above 400 ft gross height, using maximum continuous thrust. The minimum gradient capability for the specimen aeroplane is given as 1.4%, which will be achieved at a gross gradient available at 400 ft of not less than 3.2%.

The method used to solve this type of problem is illustrated by the graph in Diagram 6.2; again the diagram is not to scale and is descriptive only.

Diagram 6.2

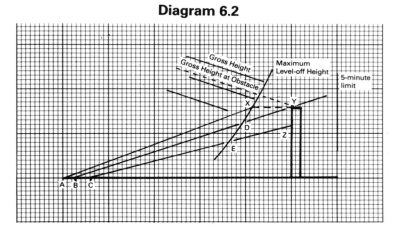

Obstacle distance from reference zero: 15,500 m
Obstacle height above reference zero: 1300 ft
Wind component: Nil

Gross gradient available at 400 ft — greater than 3.2% — CEZ does not clear obstacle, and is beyond the maximum level-off height.

At obstacle height (1300 ft), at the maximum level-off height, gross height = 1740 ft, and gradient required to clear obstacle = 4.3% = AX.

At the obstacle distance and obstacle height (gross height = 1800 ft) the gradient required to clear the obstacle, extending the second-segment climb = four per cent = BDY. Clearly, the extended second-segment procedure allows a greater take-off weight than the previous procedure. Where the obstacle lies beyond the maximum level-off line, the effect of the change in obstacle distance as weight is reduced, although ever present, is considered to be insignificant.

It may be noted in both Diagam 6.2 and Figure 20 that the gross height required, using the extended second segment, exceeds the gross height where the gradient required/available intercepts the maximum level-off line; this is the main method by which the need for an extended second segment may be identified, subject, of course, to the five minute time limit. When converted to a pressure altitude increment (Fig 26) and added to the aerodrome pressure altitude, the gross (level-off) height defines the start of the third segment, using the altimeter.

When extracting the gross height for level-off purposes, care should be taken in selecting the correct height (eg given an obstacle at 10,000 m (nil wind) and 800 ft, and assuming a gross gradient available at 400 ft of four per cent, the gross height for levelling-off and clearing the obstacle would be approximately 1090 ft, and **not** 1230 ft, the latter being the gross height at the obstacle if the climb was continued at the available gradient.

(e) Improved Obstacle Clearance — Increased V2

The title of this procedure is rather misleading as the only improvement made is in take-off weight, and even then on a marginal basis when compared with normal procedures. Appendix 5 shows that when the take-off weight is limited by something other than the field length available, some of the unused field length could be used in achieving an enhanced take-off weight, with an increased V2 in proportion to the weight increase, thus attaining a slightly better second-segment climb performance. That limit was due to WAT — the maximum take-off weight at which, for the pressure altitude and temperature, the minimum required climb gradient can be met.

In this procedure, the take-off weight is again limited by something other than the available field length, which also requires a minimum climb gradient to be met (eg an obstacle). Therefore, in this procedure the WAT limit in the 'normal' increased V2 procedure is substituted by the obstacle limit.

The method used for this procedure is adequately covered in CAP 385, Example 6, and it is interesting to note, that had the problem been processed by using the normal weight reduction method (eg using the trade lines), the obstacle limited weight would have been 169,500 kg; whereas with this procedure the obstacle limited weight is given as 172,000 kg. With the enhanced weight, and increasing the V2 some of the previously unused field length will be used — TODR will increase and the gradient available will decrease.

The gradient decrease is shown as a function of the speed increase, which is used to 'recover' the gradient loss, and provide a slightly better second-segment performance. It will be remembered from (c) that the function of the trade lines was, in conjunction with establishing an obstacle clearance gradient, to change the obstacle distance from reference zero in proportion to the gradient change. In this procedure it is assumed that reference zero remains at the end of the maximum usable clearway, bearing in mind the increased TODR for the enhanced weight and increased speed, thus ignoring the trade lines.

The methods of calculating the various operating speeds are similar to those outlined in Appendix 5.

(f) **Turns in the Flight Path**
As indicated in 6.13.2 and CAP 385 p.27, a turn or turns in the take-off flight path may only be planned for the

second and/or fourth segments, although, in practice, a pilot may opt to make a turn at any time, providing limitations are observed. In relation to airspeed, when planning a turn or turns, the main speeds to be considered would be V2 for the second segment, and V2 + 70 kt for the fourth segment.

Also associated with the segment(s) under consideration is flap configuration, in conjunction with the angle of bank which, for all planned turns, is assumed to be no less than fifteen degrees. The output from the foregoing criteria is the gradient decrement in a planned turn, and is given in Figure 24 of CAP 385. Again, as far as planning is concerned the two vital values obtained from the given figure are 0.24%, when the flaps are fully retracted in the fourth segment; and 0.7%, when the flaps are still extended in the second segment.

All necessary turn data is contained in Figure 25 of CAP 385, and using that data the following example is calculated:

Aerodrome pressure altitude:	2500 ft
OAT:	+25°C
Runway in use:	36
Reported wind component:	Nil
Take-off weight:	185,000 kg
ACS packs:	On

The standard instrument departure requires a turn to be completed before the end of the second segment on to a track of 070°(M). The turn is to start overhead a fan marker, at 4500 m from the end of TODA.

The start and finishing heights of the turn need to be calculated.

(i)	Fig 16 Second segment, therefore V2= 157 kt	
(ii)	Fig 25 radius of turn:	= 2800 m
(iii)	angle of turn:	70°
	Fig 25 distance travelled in turn:	3400 m
(iv)	Fig 25 Time in turn:	40 secs
(v)	Fig 18 Climb gradient before turn:	3.4%
(vi)	Fig 20 Gross/net height before turn:	
	510 ft/347 + 35 = 382 ft	
(vii)	Fig 24 Gradient decrement (flaps 10°):	0.7%

(viii) Gross/net height after turn:

Total distance:	4500 + 3400 = 7900 m
Gross/net height at 7900 m (3.4%):	870/640 ft
Gradient decrement:	0.7%
Height lost during turn:	3400×3.28×0.007=78 ft
Gross/net height after turn:	870 − 78 = 792 ft 640 − 78 = 562 ft

It should be appreciated that, in addition to planning the avoidance of an obstacle by turning, effectively the flight path is being planned to 'bend', so that the obstacle may well be outside the flight path area (the funnel), and consequently may not require the regulatory clearance. However, if the obstacle should still be in the flight path area during the turn, then the obstacle clearance is increased to fifty feet whilst turning.

Determining the point at which a turn should start can be carried out as follows:

Example:
A range of hills 1500 ft above field level crosses the flight path at 10,000 m from reference zero (TODA 3000 m).

Assuming the aeroplane to be in the second segment after take-off from an aerodrome, at 2500 ft pressure altitude, with an ambient temperature of +20°C. determine the point at which the turn should start.

Funnel = 10,000/8 + 84 = 1334 m.
Therefore use 900 m (maximum)
V2 at take-off weight 190,000 kg = 158.5 kt.
Radius of turn = 3000 m.
Aeroplane must turn at 3000 m (R of T) + 900 m = 3900 m before obstacle.
Obstacle at 10,000 m from reference zero = 13,000 m from brake release.
Therefore, turn must start at 13,000 − 3900 = 9100 after brake release.

To complete the calculations, assuming ACS packs are off and a nil wind component.

Gradient before turn:	3.35% (Fig 18 temperature +24°C)

Start of turn:	9300 − 3000 = 6300 m from reference zero
Gross/net height:	700/515 ft
Distance travelled in turn:	4700 m (turn 90°)
Total distance:	4700 + 6300 = 11,000 m
Gross/net height (3.35%):	1150/820 ft
Decrement:	4700 × 3.28 × 0.007 = 108 ft
Gross/net height after turn:	1042/712 ft

Note, that in both examples given, the height determined at the end of the turn is predicated mainly on the gradient decrement applicable to the distance travelled during the turn; this height decrement is then subtracted from the gross/net heights attained at the total distance travelled at the gross gradient at 400 ft. The gross gradient at 400 ft is not decreased by the gradient decrement and used to find the height gained during a turn, because the rate of change of height is not linear for a given gradient, and also, the gradient given, applies to 400 ft.

Turn problems relating to the final segment may be solved in a similar manner to those given in this book, using, in addition to Figure 26, Figures 22, 23 and 24 in conjunction with Example 5 of CAP 385.

Appendix 7

Operations involving contaminated runways Reference CAP 385 — Appendix 2

The risks, factors involved, and implications of operating on runways contaminated by water, slush, or wet and dry snow are covered in 6.7, and it is suggested that the section, including hydroplaning, be reviewed before proceeding further. This appendix, in conjunction with the CAP reference above and the associated graphs will concentrate on determining the critical weights and speeds associated with these operations.

However, before considering the procedures used, some important aspects need to be reiterated:

(a) Operations involving contaminated runways should be avoided whenever possible.

(b) Flight Manual performance data related to such operations should be regarded as advisory only (the best data available).

(c) Safety margins, provided on a normal take-off to take account of engine failure, are not available for contaminated runways, as it is assumed that all engines are operating throughout the take-off.

(d) Most Flight Manuals contain advisory data relating to the determination of a maximum speed for abandoning a take-off; this speed should **not** be regarded as a V1, as it implies no capability of continuing the take-off in the event of engine failure and, unlike V1, it could be less than Vmcg.

Among the problems outlined in 6.7 are those related to the deterioration of acceleration and braking performance, due respectively to impact drag, and decreased friction between the tyres and runway. These problems may be resolved as follows:

Aerodrome pressure altitude:	4000 ft
OAT:	0°C
TORA:	3200 m
EDA:	3300 m

TODA:	3500 m
Runway Slope:	Nil
Reported wind component:	10 kt head
ACS packs:	Off
Tyre speed rating:	225 mph
Obstacles:	Nil

Calculations

Fig 8 Runway correction (all engines operating):	3640 m
Fig 9 EDA correction:	3460 m
Fig 11 Runway correction (one engine inoperative):	3450 m
V1/VR:	0.917
Fig 12 Field length limited take-off weight:	196,500 kg
WAT limited take-off weight:	192,500 kg
Tyre speed limiting weight:	Not limiting
Maximum permitted take-off weight:	192,500 kg
Fig 16 Speeds: 192,500 kg/0.917	
V1 wet: 141.5 kt	
V1 dry: 152.5 kt	
VR: 154.5 kt	
V2: 159 kt	
Vmcg: 110 kt	
Fig 17 Brake energy speed:	163 kt

Assume the runway becomes contaminated by 15 mm of standing water.

Due allowance must be made for:

(a)   contaminant impingement drag

(b)   abandoning the take-off in the event of an emergency.

For (a) the allowance is made by correcting the distance D available for take-off weight, at the same time allowing for the differing effects of each of the contaminants because, as will be seen, for acceleration and continuation of take-off following engine failure, slush and snow are deemed to be worse than water. For (b), all contaminants are deemed to have the same effect (the runway is treated as being icy, or very slippery).

It has been stated in 6.7.4 that predicting or measuring the actual coefficient of friction, or the value of contaminent displacement and impingement drag is very difficult; making the accurate scheduling of performance data equally difficult.

However, for the specimen aeroplane, some endeavour has been made to distinguish between the different types of contaminants, by guiding the assessor to use the appropriate data. This is achieved by first determining the hydroplaning speed, remembering that this speed will in fact vary according to type of contaminant. The assessor is guided according to the relative value of hydroplaning speed, in comparison with the original VR determined. It should be noted that this procedure is peculiar to the specimen aeroplane only; other Performance Group A aeroplanes' procedures may be quite different.

Using the given data, the hydroplaning speed (Vp) (using water as the contaminant, and the given conditions) is 133 kt (note: the Vp is **not** dependent on aeroplane weight), and is the speed at which the onset of hydroplaning can be expected to occur. In comparison with the VR initially determined (154.5 kt) it is found to be less than Vp, and because of this the performance assessor is advised to use a specific chart — Chart A (Figure 33).

Because a continued take-off is predicated on all engines operating, one of the parameters used on the chart is the 'all engines operating' distance D (extracted from Figure 8 in the initial calculations — 3640 m). Another parameter is the type of contaminant and its associated depth — in this case 15 mm of water.

Using these values, the distance D available for take-off weight on the contaminated runway is determined as 2470 m which, as can be seen, is a considerable reduction from the 3450 m originally used. The extracted distance D is then used to determine the maximum permitted take-off weight, appropriate to the contaminated runway (in this case 171,200 kg — Figure 12).

As a result, the reduction in acceleration caused by 15 mm of standing water is equivalent to reducing the take-off weight by 21,300 kg — quite a significant reduction. It should be noted that the distance D extracted from Chart A is termed 'Distance D in Slush'; this does **not** mean that the runway is contaminated by slush, but is the term used to denote a distance appropriate to a contaminated runway.

In terms of stopping, the runway is considered to be 'very slippery', and the distance available must be corrected to allow for the decreased coefficient of friction. This is carried out on a specific figure, which is only used for this condition — Figure 10. Using the original EDA data (3300 m), the corrected EDA appropriate to the slippery conditions is found to be 2420 m which, again, is a considerable reduction from the corrected EDA of 3460 m in normal conditions.

The distance D in slush (2470 m) and the slippery runway corrected EDA (2420 m) will provide from Figure 11 a V1/VR value of 0.895. Although using the term and method of determining a V1, the V1/VR so found will not provide a V1 when converted to a speed; it will however provide an approximation to the maximum speed from which a safe stop may be made with all engines operating — Vstop. To complete the performance assessment the critical speeds are determined from Figure 16, using the given aerodrome data and the maximum permitted take-off weight of 171,200 kg:

$$VR = 144.5 \text{ kt}$$
$$V2 = 151.5 \text{ kt}$$
$$Vstop = 0.895$$
$$VR = 129 \text{ kt}$$
$$Vmcg = 110 \text{ kt}$$

Assuming the runway was contaminated by 15 mm of slush, a similar procedure to that outlined is followed but, as will be seen, in this case the Vp is calculated as 157.5 kt. This is greater than the original VR determined, so the assessor is advised to use Chart B — Figure 34. Using the appropriate parameters the distance D in slush is found to be 2170 m, which is 300 m less than the distance for 15 mm of water.

It can now be seen how the different characteristics of the contaminants are taken into account when considering the effect of impingement drag on aeroplane acceleration, producing, in this case, a maximum permitted take-off weight in slush of 161,000 kg. Using the distance D in slush of 2170 m, and the corrected EDA, previously found, of 2470 m, Figure 11 will provide a V1/VR of 0.942 to determine Vstop which in this case is 131 kt (VR = 139 kt). Thus the more detrimental effect of slush — unlike water — is taken into account and produces a considerable reduction in maximum permitted take-off weight.

It may have been noted that when determining the Vp for slush, the speed found could so easily have been less than the VR, and would then have led the assessor to use Chart A instead of Chart B; although this would have depended on the wind component and temperature deviation used for the given pressure altitude. For instance, had the wind component been zero, the Vp would have been determined as 148 kt, resulting in the use of Chart A, which is not as critical as Chart B.

However, it should be remembered that the same wind component must be applied to all parameters so that, initially, the 'all engines operating' distance D (Fig 8) would have been 3500 m which, when used on Chart A provides a distance D in slush of 2390 m, in turn giving a maximum permitted take-off weight of 168,500 kg — 2700 kg less than that calculated using a 10 kt headwind. Should the Vp determined equal the VR, then it would be prudent to use the more restrictive distance obtained from Chart B.

Assuming the runway was contaminated by 15 mm of wet snow, then Chart B would certainly have been used, because the Vp determined for this contaminant, for nominal aerodrome altitudes, temperatures and wind components would be in the region of 175–185 kt; for the case in question, it is determined as 181 kt, requiring similar treatment to the slush case.

For very dry snow, the assessor is instructed to use Chart B. (It is interesting to note here the comparative depths of dry snow and the other contaminants, also the applicability of the given Chart.)

For take-off from an ice-covered runway, the procedures and provisions are adequately covered in CAP 385 p.20. Using the given data therein, the maximum permitted take-off weight would have been determined as 192,000 kg and, using the corrected EDA of 2420 m, the V1/VR for such conditions is determined as 0.807. With VR at 154 kt, Vstop is calculated as 124 kt.

Landing on a contaminated runway

For landing on a contaminated runway the hydroplaning speed can be calculated from the figure already given. However, where landing weight/distances are to be determined the table on page 31 of CAP 385 will provide distances appropriate to the quoted coefficient of friction. It should be remembered that, when calculating weights, the distances available are decreased but when determining distances, these must be enhanced according to the table published on page 31.

Should doubt exist concerning any aspect of contaminated runway operations, the take-off should be delayed until **all** problems are solved satisfactorily. For landing, a hold may suffice to allow conditions to improve, otherwise a diversion may well be the safer alternative.

In all cases, operations involving contaminated runways should be avoided whenever possible, by all classes of aeroplane.

Glossary

Altitudes

Pressure Altitude
The height in the International Standard Atmosphere at which the prevailing pressure occurs; obtained by setting the sub-scale of a pressure altimeter to 1013.2 mb (29.92 in/760 mm mercury).

Restarting Altitude
The altitude up to which it has been demonstrated possible to restart an aeroplane's power unit (engine) safely and reliably.

Heights

Gross Height
The true height attained at any point in the take-off flight path, determined by using gross climb performance data, and used to determine pressure altitude for obstacle clearance and initiation of flap retraction.

Height
The vertical distance between the lowest part of the aeroplane and the relevant datum.

Net Height
The true height attained at any point in the take-off flight path, using net climb performance data. Used to determine the net flight path which must clear all obstacles by at least thirty-five feet, in order to comply with the regulations.

Screen Height
A height of thirty-five/fifty feet above the runway after take-off, and at thirty/fifty feet above the runway on approaching to land. It is assumed that the aeroplane is in an unbanked attitude, with the landing gear extended. (Note: thirty-five/fifty feet after take-off refers to Performance Group A aeroplanes and other performance groups respectively; whilst thirty/fifty feet not only refers to different performance groups, but also to different methods in calculating the landing distance required.)

Miscellaneous

Alternate Aerodrome
An aerodrome at which the aeroplane may land if a landing at an intended aerodrome becomes inadvisable.

Bleed Air
Air taken from the compressor stage(s) of the engine(s), and used to operate other systems on the aeroplane (eg air conditioning, and pressurization).

Braking Coefficient of Friction
The ratio between the tyre friction force and the vertical load on the tyre.

Engine Pressure Ratio (EPR)
A ratio of pressures of certain engine parameters indicated to the pilot and used for setting thrust.

Public Transport Flight
An aeroplane in flight shall be deemed to fly for the purpose of public transport if any passengers or cargo are carried gratuitously in the aircraft on that flight. A more detailed definition is given in ANO Article 96 (A). For practical purposes associated with this guide, it may be considered to be a flight to which the weight and performance regulations strictly apply, except for training flights.

Performance

Gradient/Slope
Inclination to the horizontal, expressed as a percentage. The term 'slope' is used with reference to aerodrome surfaces; whereas 'gradient' refers to climb or descent profiles.

Gross Performance
The average performance which a fleet of aeroplanes should achieve if maintained and operated satisfactorily in accordance with the Approved Flight Manual (AFM).

Net Performance
The gross performance having been reduced to allow for various contingencies which cannot be accounted for operationally. Provided that the aeroplane is operated in accordance

with the recommended techniques, the net performance should be exceeded.

Speeds

Airspeed Indicator Reading (ASIR)
The uncorrected reading on a specified airspeed indicator.

All Engines Screen Speed (V3)
The speed at which the aeroplane is assumed to pass through the screen height with all engines operating on take-off.

Brake Energy Speed (Vmbe)
The maximum speed on the ground from which a stop can be accomplished within the energy capabilities of the brakes.

Calibrated Airspeed (CAS)
The indicated speed of an aeroplane, corrected for position and instrument error. It is equal to the true airspeed in the standard atmosphere at sea level, and at any pressure altitude/temperature combination giving zero density altitude.

Decision Speed (V1)
An engine failure being promptly recognised, it is the speed at which the continued take-off distance and take-off run will not exceed the TODA and TORA, respectively; and at which the accelerate-stop distance (emergency distance required) will not exceed the EDA.

Engine Failure Speed (Vef)
The CAS at which the critical engine is assumed to fail.

Equivalent Airspeed (EAS)
The calibrated airspeed, corrected for adiabatic compressible flow for a particular altitude. It is equal to the CAS in standard atmosphere at sea level.

Indicated Airspeed (IAS)
The airspeed shown on the pitot/static airspeed indicator, calibrated to reflect standard atmosphere adiabatic compressible flow at sea level, uncorrected for airspeed system errors.

Lift-off Speed (Vlof)
In relation to CAS, the speed at which the aeroplane first becomes airborne.

Minimum Control Speed (Vmca)

The minimum flight speed at which the aeroplane is controllable with a maximum five degrees of bank, when the critical engine becomes inoperative, with the remaining engines at take-off thrust.

Minimum Control Speed — Ground (Vmcg)

The minimum speed on the ground at which the take-off can be continued safely when the critical engine becomes inoperative, with the remaining engines at take-off thrust.

Minimum Control Speed — Landing (Vmcl)

In an approach or landing configuration, the minimum speed at which it is possible, with one engine inoperative, to maintain control of the aeroplane within defined limits, while applying variations of power.

Minimum Unstick Speed (Vmu)

The minimum speed at which it is possible to leave the ground with all engines operating, and climb without due hazard.

Power Failure Speed Ratio (V1/VR)

The ratio appropriate to the two speeds for a given aeroplane weight and aerodrome characteristics, introduced into performance assessment for convenience, and used to determine V1 — decision speed.

Rectified Airspeed (RAS)

Indicated airspeed, corrected for pressure error.

Rotation Speed (VR)

The speed at which the pilot starts to rotate the aeroplane for take-off. It is a function of aeroplane weight and flap setting, but can also vary with pressure altitude and temperature.

Steady Initial Climb Speed (V4)

The 'all engines operating' take-off climb speed, used to the point where acceleration to flap retraction speed is initiated; it should be attained by 400 ft above aerodrome level.

Take-off Safety Speed (V2)

The lowest speed at which the aeroplane complies with those handling cirteria associated with the climb after take-off, following engine failure. Also, the target speed to be attained at the screen height and used to the point where acceleration to flap retraction speed is initiated.

Target Threshold Speed (Vat)
The speed at which the pilot should aim to cross the runway threshold to ensure that the scheduled landing field lengths are consistently achieved.
Speeds at the threshold are:
  (a) Vato — all engines operating
  (b) Vat1 — a critical engine inoperative
  (c) Vat max (Maximum Threshold Speed) — the speed at the threshold above which the risk of exceeding the scheduled landing field length is unacceptably high. Go-around action should normally be taken if it appears that this speed will be exceeded; usually, Vato + 15 kt.

True Airspeed (TAS)
The speed of the aeroplane relative to the undisturbed air. Obtained by correcting EAS for density.

Vsl
As Vso, but with the aeroplane in a configuration appropriate to the case under consideration.

Vso
A stalling speed (or if a stalling speed is unobtainable, a minimum steady flight speed) EAS, with wing flaps in the landing configuration.

Temperatures
Declared Temperature
The appropriate average monthly temperature, plus half its deviation from ISA.

Indicated Air Temperature/Total Air Temperature (TAT)
The static air temperature, plus adiabatic compression (ram) rise, as indicated on the Total Air Temperature Indicator.

International Standard Atmosphere (ISA)
The interrelation of the air temperature and pressure altitude. For JAR and BCAR, the following is acceptable:
  (a) the air is a perfect gas
  (b) the temperature at sea level is +15°C
  (c) the pressure at sea level is 1013.2 mb (29.92 in)

(d) the temperature gradient from sea level to the altitude at which the temperature becomes −56.5°C is 1.98°C/1000 ft

(e) the density at sea level under the above conditions is 1.225 kg/m^3.

Outside Air Temperature (OAT)
The free static (ambient) temperature.

Weights

Landing Weight
The weight of the aeroplane at the time of landing, taking into account the weights of fuel and oil expected to be used on the flight to the aerodrome at which the landing is to be effected.

Maximum Take-off Weight (MTOW)
The maximum weight at which take-off is permitted by conditions other than available performance.

Maximum Landing Weight
The maximum weight at which landing is permitted (other than in an emergency) by considerations other than available performance.

Maximum Total Weight Authorised (MTWA)
The maximum total weight of the aeroplane and its contents, at which it may take off anywhere in the world, in the most favourable circumstances, and in accordance with the certificate of airworthiness in force at the time.

Maximum Zero Fuel Weight
The weight of the aeroplane, above which all weight must comprise fuel. The limitation is determined by structural airworthiness requirements.

Regulated Take-off Weight (RTOW)
The maximum permitted take-off weight of the aeroplane at the start of the take-off run, derived by complying with all the requirements of the weight and performance regulations appropriate to the flight. Often used loosely to indicate a weight which would satisfy only one aspect of the regulations, and therefore should always be qualified.

Take-off Weight (TOW)
The gross weight of the aeroplane at the start of the take-off run.

Weight, Altitude, and Temperature (WAT)
Conditions of aeroplane weight which, when combined with aerodrome pressure altitude and temperature, reduce the performance level to the relevant airworthiness minima.

Diagrams — Appendices

Figures

Tables